GREENHOUSE MANAGEMENT

for

Flower and Plant Production

KENNARD S. NELSON, B.A., M.S., Ph.D.

Formerly Extension Specialist in Floriculture
The Ohio State University

GREENHOUSE
MANAGEMENT

for Flower and Plant Production

THE INTERSTATE PRINTERS & PUBLISHERS, INC.
Danville, Illinois

PREFACE

Much of the greenhouse managers' work for flower and plant production has to be involved in crop rotations and scheduling. In the discusson of it in Chapter 4 as many illustrations as possible have been used to show how this work is done. There are no printed forms available for the manager to use. He has to rule his own form for the specific job and make the necessary entries. The illustrations provided are reproductions of rotations and schedules as the foreman might make them.

It was felt that the cultural aspects of the business should be approached from two broad fronts—the soil environment and the air environment. This approach was made in order to stress the interrelation of the portions of each environment and to show how a change in one component can affect others. The restrictive legislation which has been placed on the use of agricultural chemicals makes it impossible to discuss the specifics of their use in a publication of this type. For the foreseeable future it appears that their use will have to be based directly on label registration; and that detail, or rather the rapidly changing details, cannot be covered in a book.

Business procedures, engineering, and marketing are not discussed frequently in books for flower growers. However, these important parts of the business do need some recognition, and it is hoped that the introductory remarks made in each of these subjects plus the reference reviews will be helpful.

KENNARD S. NELSON

Columbus, Ohio

TABLE OF CONTENTS

CHAPTER 1

What Is a Manager?

CHAPTER 1

A manager is an organizer, a planner, a person capable of great capacity for work, a decision maker, a diplomat, a problem solver, a firm believer that all activities must be for the betterment of the business, a person of good judgement and one who is knowledgeable, honest and forthright, and challenged by the accomplishment of the job.

There is no attempt here to make a manager sound superhuman, but it should be recognized that certain qualities are essential. It may not be possible to get all of these qualities rolled into each manager, and there is an advantage in listing them in order of importance for the job. There can be no compromise on honesty—at any level of management—and all managers must be able to think and reason. Theirs is not a job of performing tasks by rote, but one of decision making and judgement. The individual who is not able to make up his mind, or does not want to, should remain a worker. The manager needs to put everything into perspective and make the arrangements for first things to be done first. He has to be a selfless individual who will consider the welfare of the company and those under him before he will consider his own. A good manager will often be bored with and uninspired by the performance of routine activities himself but will recognize the importance of and enjoy the development of the routines that are so necessary in conducting the work.

It should be understood that there are individuals who desire to become managers because they do not want to be managed. They have the mistaken concept that they can become successful managers by enjoying the privileges but shirking the responsibilities. It does not take long to discover their lack of real managerial qualities, but it would be helpful if this could be determined before the appointment was made. At the other end of the stream are the very capable workers who, because of modesty or other reasons, do not envision themselves as managers. In a certain per cent of them there will be some latent but fine managerial qualities to be uncovered.

There are various levels of management, but the basic functions of managers are essentially the same, regardless of position. Greenhouse flower and plant production businesses are relatively small business units—from single individual operation to about 100 employees. In the smaller businesses the owner may be the sole manager—a complex job because of the wide variety of activities encompassed. He may be the major part of the labor force also. Many of the greenhouse businesses started as a side venture for the family and grew as the children matured or relatives joined the organization. With such a start there is an inclination to operate rather informally and with management poorly defined. The management needs, however, remain the same regardless of the relationship of the individuals in the organization.

• THE TYPES OF ACTIVITIES IN THE BUSINESS THAT REQUIRE MANAGEMENT SHOULD BE ACKNOWLEDGED

The usual activities involved in the production of flowers and plants in the greenhouse may be grouped under four headings—business procedures, engineering, production, and marketing. In the larger organizations these divisions of activities may be recognized with department designation and individual managers. The smaller organizations may not have need for formal listing of departments, but the manager must realize that although his primary interest or training may be in production, he must maintain a vital concern for and in fact manage the other activities. The individual who becomes an owner-operator of a flower and plant production greenhouse usually got his start because of his interest in growing flowers, or in designing and selling them, or in both. In spite of specific interest, he may have to handle all activities to begin with. As the business grows he hires help where it is needed the most, and this will be either in marketing or in production. He will have to continue to take care of business procedures and engineering.

Reports and payments to various levels of government have become sufficiently involved so that a business regardless of size finds it wise to engage the help of a professional accountant just to keep straight with the government. The accountant may take care of other business procedures also, but frequently the individual businessman handles the basic paper or book work such as payroll, correspondence, accounts receivable, purchasing, accounts payable, and financial arrangements. Regardless of how this work is done the operator must make sure that it is done accurately and promptly.

The engineering is involved with the physical facilities—buildings, vehicles, equipment, and machinery. Some of this work requires special training or tools, and it should be done by professionals. Other duties can be handled by the greenhouse operator; or if he cannot take care of the original installation, he may be able to do the maintenance work. If the greenhouse man is handy with tools, he may be able to do much of the engineering work on the place more economically and promptly than if he had to hire it done.

In partnerships, frequently the primary interest of one of the partners is in the flower shop, and that of the other in the greenhouse; or if it is a wholesale flower production greenhouse, one partner may function mainly in engineering and the other in production. But for the welfare of the business they must decide who is the general manager as well as who will be responsible for the other two phases of the business.

In larger businesses there may be enough workers so that one or more foremen are used to direct the activities, and it may be advisable to organize the work by departments with departmental managers. The larger business will still be involved with business procedures, engineering, production, and marketing; but because of the size of the business and the number of people employed, a single manager cannot provide the direction that is needed.

- **THE STRUCTURE OF MANAGEMENT OR THE CHAIN OF COMMAND MUST BE UNDERSTOOD BY EVERYONE IN THE ORGANIZATION**

It may be possible for the business to function without a formal chain of command, but it certainly does encourage problems. In any business, regardless of size, the responsibility for the entire operation must rest with one individual. He must acknowledge and accept this responsibility if the business is to succeed, and those under him must understand that they take direction from him. If it is a smaller business, the relationship will be directly from owner-operator to worker, and for larger businesses the direction may be through managers to foremen to workers.

Figures 1–1 through 1–5 give possible management structures for

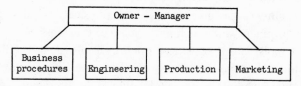

Fig. 1—1. Management structure with single manager. Regardless of the size of the business, the greenhouse manager does become involved in business procedures, engineering, production, and marketing. The single manager must be versatile if all phases of the business are to be handled well.

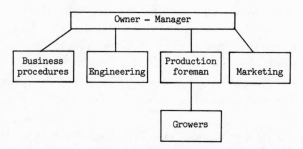

Fig. 1—2. Management structure with production foreman. With this kind of structure, the manager uses a production foreman so that he may spend more of his own time on the other phases of the business. Direction from manager to growers must be through the foreman.

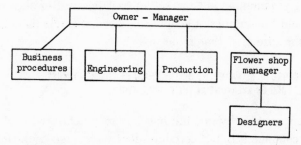

Fig. 1—3. Management structure with flower shop manager. Frequently this type of structure exists in a family-operated retail greenhouse, with the wife taking the responsibility of handling the flower shop.

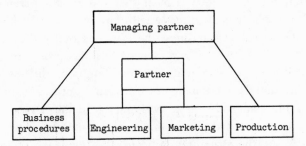

Fig. 1—4. Management structure for a partnership. It is very important to have responsibilities and authority clearly outlined in a partnership. This is only one of several possible arrangements.

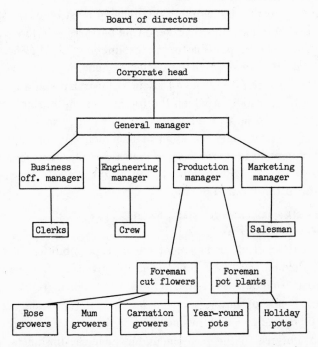

Fig. 1—5. Management structure for a corporation. Each place of business needs to develop its own management structure, based on the work to be done. Following this, assignments to positions can be made. The management structure or organizational chart has to be a written record so that reference is made easily to commitments and responsibilities.

typical owner-operator, partnership, or corporate forms of business. In the simplest structure it is clear that the owner-operator handles the work himself or deals directly with any workers that he may employ. In the greenhouse business, he usually handles the engineering himself, his wife may take care of most business procedures, and she and the children may work under his direction in production and sales. Maybe this sounds a bit more formal than is practiced in a family operation, but somebody has to be in charge if the desired objectives are going to be reached. These things do not just happen, even on a small basis. As the structures indicate, if a manager or foreman is used in flower shop or greenhouse production, the line of communication between owner and designers or growers must be through the respective manager or foreman.

In a partnership the working relationship must be clear. The illustration used here indicates that one of the partners is in fact the manager with specific responsibilities in production and business procedures, while the other partner handles engineering and marketing.

The corporate management structure illustrated could be a larger-sized family operation in which the founder of the business functions as corporate head in his later years, with his son or son-in-law as general manager, or it could represent management by unrelated individuals. The point to be made here is that a definite management structure is essential in both instances—and might possibly be even more important in the family operation.

● THE MANAGER PLANS, ORGANIZES, STAFFS, DIRECTS,
CONTROLS, AND REPRESENTS

With the job of management come responsibilities. These must be well defined, and sufficient authority given to the manager, so that he can function efficiently. It does not seem to be sensible, but there are heads of businesses who have need for managers but do not let them manage. The business suffers because the good manager will not continue in the position under such circumstances, and the poor manager will remain. This will be true at any level of management.

The manager must have the responsibility of making the plans for his section, department, or crew. Depending on the type of planning, some help will come from above; but the foreman must be in on the planning that affects him and his workers.

• PROPER ORGANIZING GIVES SMOOTH OPERATION

With plan at hand the next step is organizing so that the plan can be carried out effectively. This may be providing the necessary equipment, arranging the work area, making work assignments, and in general coordinating all elements so that the job can be handled. Most planning and organizing must precede the work, and this may require that managers' work hours be flexible enough so that their preliminaries are finished before the workers arrive. Depending upon the level of management, consideration should be given to placing the manager on salary, with self-arranged hours as the job demands.

The reason for organizing is the attainment of objectives—getting the job done. The work force needs to be divided into units which can function efficiently. The division will depend on the kind and type of work being done. The more people that are employed, the greater the need for organization. But regardless of size, every superior in the organization must be responsible for the acts of those under him. The success or failure in handling the job lies directly with the manager, and this will be determined by the way he utilizes the men and tools at his disposal. He cannot delegate any of this responsibility. It is solely his, but he can and must delegate enough authority to those under him so the job can be done properly.

Each subordinate in the organization must have only one superior. This is true for small family operations as well as large, complex organizations. If the kids get instructions from both Mom and Pop on what to do or how to do it, the work will be ineffective. When the general manager short circuits his production manager by going directly to the growers with directives, he makes it impossible for the production manager to do his job. Somehow or other superiors need to relax and have faith in the people under them—give them a chance to use their own ideas and methods even if some mistakes are made.

• THE MANAGER CHOOSES, TRAINS, AND PROMOTES OR RELEASES HIS OWN STAFF

The primary need for a manager is for the coordination of the work effort of the individuals under him. Part of his responsibility should be the staffing of his section or department. The start here should be in defining the job requirements. What capabilities do his workers need? He then selects (hires) the individuals who fill the requirements the best, gives them whatever training is needed, promotes them if their skills develop properly, and releases them if they do not perform satisfactorily. The manager should have this responsibility for these functions, and he needs the authority to carry them out effectively.

● BY LEADERSHIP THE MANAGER PROVIDES THE DIRECTION NEEDED

In directing the individuals under him the manager must communicate with them effectively, give them leadership or guidance, and so motivate them that the job is accomplished. Communication is no small task. Sometimes there is an actual language problem when foreign workers are used. There even may be varying degrees of understanding among those who speak the same tongue. It is difficult to know for certain when understanding has been reached. The manager needs to develop some routine checks to make sure that the instructions have been understood.

If the manager is an effective leader, he will have the respect of those under him. This respect may derive from his superior knowledge of his job, his organizational ability, clarity of communication, gentlemanliness and fairness, or understanding of his workers.

Workers will be motivated in various ways—some merely by understanding that the job is there for the doing. Others may be motivated if they have more knowledge of how the job is to be done or why it is being done. Their interest may be aroused if they understand how their work fits in with that in other departments, or there may be some element of competition developed between groups doing the same type of work in different areas. Many workers will be motivated if they believe their monetary compensation is based on the quality or quantity of work they do. There probably should be a pay scale established so that for each type of job there is a starting wage and a maximum wage, and there may be provisions for one or more raises between the two. For each job there should be a set period of time after the individual is hired, after which he is either given a raise or is released—possibly something like two months. This is a method for retaining the potentially good workers and separating out the less likely ones, for their own good as well as for the welfare of the company.

The motivating effects of fringe benefits are questionable. Some workers will respond to them; others eventually look upon them as a necessary company expense with no material value to them personally. There is an inclination among workers to remember only the net amount of weekly pay and to forget that each week they also receive compensation in money withheld to pay their income tax, paid hospitalization, insurance, uniforms, or other fringes.

- THE CONTROL SYSTEM EVALUATES JOB ACCOMPLISHMENT

Managerial control is the measurement and correction of performance. The best plans may be made, the finest organizing done, and an adequate staff given good direction, but the manager needs to evaluate the results. It cannot be assumed that everything worked out all right. This must be determined while the work is being done and when the job is completed. In order to have an effective control, standards must be established. The performance then can be checked against the standard. If there is deviation from the standard, the cause must be determined and corrected. Possibly it was faulty planning, or maybe personnel problems. If possible, a running control should be used so that adjustments can be made as the problems occur.

Budgets may be used as control devices, and probably they should be used more frequently than they are. Budgets are in numerical terms, but not always in dollars. They are estimates or predictions for the future. They may be revenue and expenditure budgets in which the sales for the department or company are projected for a period of time, or they may be a projection of expenses. Budgets force a declaration of the direction the business is expected to take and the amount of money that should be involved. They can be planning devices as well as methods of control.

Some budgets will be used for time, space, material, or manpower. These will also be numerical, but usually not in dollars. Other budgets will be in monetary terms such as capital expenditure budgets and cash budgets which forecast cash receipts and disbursements. Although budgets are fine planning and control tools for the manager, it must be recognized that budget flexibility is necessary. Budgets are guideposts that may need some realignment because actual experience may have reason to vary from the forecast, and the manager will need to make this evaluation.

● **THE BUSINESS NEEDS GOOD REPRESENTATION**

The manager represents the company—for the matter at hand, he is the company. His beliefs, appearance, actions, and words will be completely compatible with those of the company.

Reference Reviews

1. Haynes, W. Warren, and Joseph L. Massie, *Management Analysis Concepts and Cases*, Second Edition, Prentice-Hall, Inc., Englewood Cliffs, New Jersey, 1969. *There is a wealth of management information in this book, but it is quite detailed and pertains largely to big business. Chapter 5, "Traditional Principles of Organization and a Modern Synthesis," and Chapter 9, "Motivation, Incentives, and Morale," probably will be of most interest to greenhouse managers.*
2. Koontz, Harold, and Cyril O'Donnell, *Principles of Management: An Analysis of Managerial Functions*, Fourth Edition, McGraw-Hill Book Company, New York, 1968. *A fine basic coverage of business management with chapters on the basis of management, planning, organizing, staffing, directing, controlling, and managers in the changing environment. The subject is presented clearly, and the application to the flower and plant production business is apparent.*

CHAPTER 2

Management of Business
Procedures

CHAPTER 2

The business needs a name, and it helps if the same name is used throughout. In the greenhouse flower and plant production business, it is not unusual for an individual to start the business as a side line and use his personal name for the business, too. Later when he decides that the business is a going concern he may choose a name which may or may not include his name, Then as sons or relatives join the firm still another business name may be coined. The result is that the business being operated at the same stand may be referred to by two or three names, and this does lead to confusion.

Games are played with addresses also. Possibly the home address was used initially, and then later the adjacent greenhouse assumed an address and it is used. Or possibly postal box numbers and street addresses are used interchangeably. The place of business needs an address which functions for postal purposes and an address that can be used for truck shipments or other deliveries. A single address will suffice if postal and truck deliveries are made to the same address, but if a postal box or rural route designation is used, this will be suitable only for postal purposes. The shipping address for truck deliveries needs to be an actual street address if there is one—or in rural communities it may include reference to highway intersections or the number of miles in a direction from a known point on a highway.

The telephone listing should be in the business name.

- **THE BUSINESS MAY BE OPERATED AS A PROPRIETORSHIP, PARTNERSHIP, OR CORPORATION**

An individual may elect to use his own resources, or those that he borrows, and operate a business under his own terms as an individual proprietorship. It is an informal business arrangement which

15

may be suitable for smaller operations. He does have unlimited liability because the law recognizes no distinction between the proprietor's business and his personal affairs.

Two or more individuals may be involved in a partnership. This is a formal contract between the partners and is enforceable at law. It is a pooling of resources, rights, and obligations of the partners. The partnership may own property in its own name, but the liability of any one partner is not limited to his investment in the business. As in a proprietorship, there is no distinction between business and personal affairs, and any and all partners are liable for debts arising from the partnership operations.

The corporation is a complex form of organization. It operates under charter granted by the state and has no rights other than those listed in the charter. Ownership of the corporation may be rather limited or may be infinitely subdivided, and this ownership is evidenced by certificates which represent shares of capital stock. The owners are not personally liable for the obligations of the corporation. The corporation is controlled by the board of directors whose members are elected by the share owners, or stockholders.

• THE OWNER MANAGES BUSINESS PROCEDURES

For larger organizations, the owner will need to have one or more managers for the various business procedures required in the operation of the business. In addition he will need to engage help in accounting matters regularly and in legal matters periodically—regardless of the size of the business. It is paper work that will be done in the office, and people are needed here that have that kind of proficiency. They will know how to handle typewriters and office machines, what forms to use, how to file information, and general office procedures. They often wear white collars, but they usually will not and should not be expected to make general management decisions.

The business office frequently is the locale for management decisions, but this is because there is easy access there to the records on which these decisions must be based. The clerks, bookkeepers, accountants, and possibly the lawyer function in accumulating the information and getting it in proper form, but it is the head of the business and the managers under him that will have to make the management decisions, because they are really the only ones that can properly evaluate the compiled information and reports.

- **BUSINESS PROCEDURES INVOLVE COMMUNICATING, PURCHASING, BILLING, PAYING, POSTING, FINANCING, COSTING, AND ANALYZING**

Somehow or other a business operation small or big has some vital functions in all of these procedures, and the way in which they are handled can be equally as important as the engineering, production, and marketing phases of the business. Communication both internal and external must be good. The internal communication is concerned primarily with reporting between the business office and engineering, production, and marketing. The paper work and tabulation done in the business office are based on reports from the other sections of the business. There must be a good understanding of form and timeliness of report and the effects on business procedures. The business office does not belong in the chain of command between the head of the business and the other departments. The internal communication between business office and the other departments will relate only to paper work and the handling of it for the benefit of the company. Directives on the operation of engineering, production, or marketing will not be routed through the business office. The business head, who thinks he might save some of his time if he passes directives to the production foreman through the office clerk or bookkeeper, will learn eventually that the office personnel are relaying their version of the message and making judgement and decisions on production matters based on their knowledge of typing or book work.

External communication is the link between the business and the outside world. The business procedures should include the facility to type a letter on business stationery and talk sensibly and politely on the telephone. If there is a business office, this communication is handled by the personnel there, but this in no way implies that the individual who types the letter is the one who writes it. Clerks and bookkeepers have their specialties, but among them is not the formulation of external communication unless it relates specifically to their field.

The external communication will usually be with the head of the company or the managers of production or marketing.

- **PURCHASING FOR THE ENTIRE ORGANIZATION SHOULD BE COORDINATED IN THE BUSINESS OFFICE**

A routine should be established for purchasing. The production foreman should know what he needs and where to get it. He should also have no doubt as to the purchasing procedure to be used in his company. Authorization for purchase needs to be handled between the head of the business and the department involved. The business office provides the proper forms, handles the paper work, and eventually makes payment. Very large firms may have a purchasing agent as part of the business office staff, and he actually handles the selection of the purchase for any of the departments. The purchasing for most flower- and plant-producing greenhouses is not extensive enough to require the services of a purchasing agent.

- **THE BUSINESS OFFICE HANDLES BILLING AND PAYING**

If the sales work is handled in an orderly way, billing becomes a routine clerical matter. Management, however, needs to establish the routine and then control it so that it operates well. Billing must be prompt. In the billing procedure a control should be established to verify that pricing and terms are correct. If cost is known on the product, it should be tabulated along with the billed price to determine if the right discount or mark-up has been used.

Paying involves payrolls and accounts payable. Management of payrolls has become quite complex because of withholding of income tax and remission to various governmental agencies. In addition, a record must be maintained of the job categories for which this pay was used. This information is essential for computing product or operation costs.

Accounts payable must be handled within the terms specified by the creditor. If there is a discount for prompt payment, this usually will be financially favorable to the debtor and should be taken. If terms are not quoted on the invoice, it may be assumed that they are 30 days. In addition to making the payment, a record must be kept which assigns the payment to the specific department, crop, or area for which it was made. This expenditure record will be used for figuring costs or in other analysis of the business.

Paying invariably is done by check because this is an orderly procedure for handling the money and includes a record of the transaction. Frequently it is the head of the business that signs the checks, but actually this is a business function any authorized member of the firm could do. Regardless of who signs the checks a routine must be used to assure that the expenditure is authorized and warranted.

- ● MANAGING ACCOUNTS RECEIVABLE HAS TO BE SOMETHING
  MORE THAN MAKING LEDGER ENTRIES

Management sets the routine for the maintenance of an accounts receivable record—equipment, forms, and personnel. It is even more important that management establishes a clear and good accounts receivable policy. A bookkeeper should be expected to do a good job of accumulating the record in the specified fashion, but he is not qualified to set general policy. This is necessarily a management decision.

Somehow or other, when the account is opened it should be determined if the customer is willing to pay and if he has the ability to pay within the terms of business. If he does not make payment when due, means need to be taken to collect the debt. This is a logical approach to handling accounts receivable, but there are some pitfalls along the route. If the procedure for opening accounts is too strict, some sales will be lost. So, each manager must devise his own method which accepts practically all of the customers who will pay and refuses most of those who will not. There is no foolproof system for selecting only good pay accounts, but there are some routines that are generally helpful. For the retail grower, his customers are local, and there should be reliable sources of credit information. When the account is opened, the name, address, and telephone number of the customer must be verified because the account must be identified with a definite individual and a reliable way to contact him must be known. At least two credit references plus the name of the customer's bank should be obtained. The customer should be advised of the terms of business and

```
                         John Doe Greenhouses
                            333 Flower St.
                            Anyplace, USA

                         ACCOUNT INFORMATION

                                                      Date_____

  Account name and address_____

         _____

         _____

  Number of years at this address _____

  Telephone number_____

  Place of employment_____

  Number of years employed there_____

  Name and address of bank_____

  Two business references


  _____          _____


  _____          _____


  _____          _____


  John Doe Greenhouses' terms of business are net 30 days.

  How would you handle your account?_____

                                Signed_____
```

Fig. 2—1. Account information form for retail customers. If it seems necessary to open accounts over the telephone, the information will be as much as or more than requested on this form, and enough time will have to be allowed for checking references.

asked if he will handle his account within those terms. It is best to have a form which can be filled out because this makes it much easier to get each piece of information in an orderly fashion. The customer's signature should be included. If it seems necessary to open accounts over the telephone, the same information should be obtained. It is advisable to verify name and address by the listing in the telephone directory, and after the references are checked the customer should be advised by telephone that the account has or has not been established.

Some retail customers prefer to do business by credit card. The

John Doe Greenhouses
333 Flower St.
Anyplace, USA

ACCOUNT INFORMATION

Date_____

Account name_____

Postal address   Shipping address

_____   _____

_____   _____

_____   _____

Telephone_____   State vendor's number_____

Form of business
  Proprietorship   Owner_____

  Partnership   Partner_____   Partner_____

  Corporation   Managing officer_____   President_____

Length of time in business under present management_____

Name and address of bank_____

Two business references

_____   _____

_____   _____

_____   _____

John Doe Greenhouses' terms of business are 1% 10 days, net 30.

How would your account be handled?_____

                              Signed_____

Fig. 2—2. Account information for wholesale customers. When an account is opened, the best possible means should be used to establish the ability and the desire of the customer to pay for his purchases within the terms of business.

retailer needs to evaluate the cost of handling accounts by this method. In most instances there is a charge to the retailer for credit card business. Some means of passing this charge along to the customer is needed. In fact there should be a policy for charging open account customers for that kind of service also. It costs less to handle the sale for cash, and the terms of business should take this into consideration. In wholesale business this frequently is recognized by terms allowing a discount for payment within a specified time—such as 2 per cent 10 days, net 30. That innocent little 2 per cent 10 days turns out to be about 24 per cent to 36 per cent interest per annum depending on whether the customer pays with order or on the tenth day. It may not be possible to use a discount for payment with order or within 10 days for retail customers. It might be more practical to place a finance charge of 1 per cent a month for purchases on open account.

Some of the wholesale flower and plant producers sell everything through one or more wholesale commission houses. These may or may not be good sales outlets, but there should not be a collection problem with them.

The wholesale grower who sells his products directly to retailers must use somewhat the same procedure as the retailer in evaluating the willingness and ability of the customer to pay within the terms of business. Included on the account information form for these customers, however, should be a question about the form of business organization. If it is a proprietorship, the name, address, and telephone number of the proprietor should be obtained. For a partnership, the names of the partners are needed, with their addresses and telephone numbers. In the case of a corporation, the names of the officers should be listed as well as the address and telephone number of the managing officer. Credit agreements and arrangements are made between the individuals authorized and responsible for the affairs of the business firm, and that is the reason it is so important to have these individuals listed on the account information sheet together with enough information for locating them.

There is general agreement that everybody knows it when an account has gone bad, but it takes an unusual credit man to tell when a good paying account is going to defer on payment and become a problem. Some customers establish an open account rating by sending payment with order or requesting C.O.D. shipments and then slipping in a few open account orders. In spite of good policies for opening accounts, some bad accounts will develop, and there needs to be a workable routine for handling them.

There is some kind of unwritten rule in the business world that although the business terms are 30 days, that actually means that payment will be accepted up to 90 days without question or penalty. Whatever the announced terms are, they should be followed. Failure to question the debtor as soon as payment is overdue is an invitation to the borderline account to become a bad account. The accounts receivable system should incorporate a method for aging accounts, and then a consistent routine should be used for bringing these accounts up to date.

The owner or manager may have a clerk or bookkeeper make entries in the accounts receivable ledger, but that does not relieve him of the responsibility of making and keeping the credit policies which will assure prompt settlement of accounts.

- **THE OWNER OR MANAGER WILL NEED SOME SOUND ADVICE FROM AN ACCOUNTANT AND A BANKER ON FINANCING**

Financing decisions must be made by management. The decisions will be based on the information accumulated in the business office, analyses of this information, budgets and estimates for the future, and general business trends. The accountant and the banker cannot make the decisions, but they can explain and interpret some of the values. This is a specialized field in which the greenhouse operator should need some professional help.

There needs to be a good working relationship between the accountant and the owner or business manager. There must be mutual respect, trust, and honesty. These two individuals have a common goal—the betterment of the business—and it takes a free blending of their information and judgement to make the best business decisions. The owner may feel that he needs only minimal help, such as handling governmental reports; or he may want assistance from the accountant in establishing product costs, developing information for budgets and business planning, and preparing summary reports for financial analysis of the business. In most instances the accountant should be used for more than preparation of governmental reports, and part of this help will be in financial management.

In a good job of financial management the cash inflow equals cash outflow. A sizeable cash balance produces liquidity and a rather comforting feeling, but it represents money that is not working and bringing a return.

It is important to monitor cash flow in the business. Inflow of cash may be from external sources, such as borrowing, or from internal means, such as cash sales, collection on accounts, or conversion of fixed assets (sale of land, equipment, structures, etc.). Outflow of cash externally is to such as interest, dividends, owner withdrawals, taxes, and repayment of debt; internally it is for purchase of fixed assets, inventories, wages, and operating and administrative expenses. An accountant can set the procedures for following the cash flow, and with the owner can plan and budget for the estimated cash flow and later analyze to determine if the flow followed the estimate or to find where adjustment is needed. If there was not the anticipated cash inflow from sales, was it lack of product, depressed prices, an increase in accounts receivable over cash sales, or a slow down in collection of accounts receivable? If the cash outflow was excessive, possibly this represented purchase of new equipment, increasing inventory, or higher operating expenses. It will be difficult to put a finger on the problem unless proper records are kept so that valid comparisons may be made which will allow sensible management decisions.

A greenhouse operator should receive as much return from the funds he has invested in his business as he might from alternative investments of similar risk. The salary he gets is in payment for the work he performs at his place of business, and as owner in addition he must get a fair rate of interest on the capital invested in fixed assets and the operation of the business. The original source of the funds is of no real concern here. Whether they came from Grandpa, from a loan company, or out of the owner's pocket, these funds must earn interest for the owner or he should invest them elsewhere.

The amount of money that a business makes should be related to the money that is invested in the business (operating assets). The operating assets consist of fixed assets (buildings, land, and equipment) plus the working capital (accounts receivable, inventory, and cash). Some honesty and judgement need to be exercised between owner and accountant to determine a realistic value for operating assets. A value has to be assigned to the fixed assets—and it needs to be a fair one. Of the working capital, inventory may not be a great consideration for greenhouse growers, and cash should be easy to determine—but accounts receivable must be viewed realistically. What per cent of the accounts are collectible? The chances are great that not 100 per cent of them can be collected. The accountant may have some clues based on business in general, but the owner should know the history of the accounts and the debtors and should be able to evaluate their worth. To get the relationship between sales and operating assets, the yearly sales are divided by the operating assets and this is referred to as turnover.

For an estimate of the earning power of a business the turnover is multiplied by the net operating margin (net operating income divided by sales). The net operating income is determined by subtracting operating expense from sales, and operating expense is cost of product, including selling costs and administration.

- **DETERMINATION OF PRODUCT COSTS ALLOWS SENSIBLE PRICING AND ADJUSTMENTS IN PRODUCTION PROCEDURES**

This is a piece of important information that needs to come out of the business. The information comes from the greenhouses. The manager and production foremen design the procedures for collecting the information and compiling it, but the computing is done in the business office because that is where the office machines are and the people to operate them. When the product costs and sales data are known, management then can interpret them, make decisions, and take the necessary action.

The specific methods for figuring product costs will have to be developed at each greenhouse, but the basics should be the same—income and expenses must be compiled by crop. Distributing income to the various crops is a fairly simple problem in bookkeeping and should not present a problem at any greenhouse. However, devising a system for relating expenses to specific crops requires some patience. There are equipment, plants, and supplies which can be charged directly to specific crops, such as chrysanthemum cuttings, pots, growth control, and sprayer used only on pot mums; also the labor on the crop can be charged directly against the crop. Other expenses, such as structure, heat, utilities, taxes, and administration, must be prorated in some fashion to the various crops.

If it is a one-crop greenhouse operation, such as all roses, compiling the labor cost is very simple; but for greenhouses with mixed crops a method must be used for assigning labor costs to the proper crops. It may be possible for each worker to report the number of hours worked per crop, or possibly this function could be handled better by the foreman.

The costs that cannot be assigned directly to a crop probably are best prorated on the basis of space occupied by the crop. Some growers like to handle this by the total amount of space under glass, and others use the total amount of bench space. Either method could be used; however, the use of bench space should be a satisfactory method and possibly easier to use. Inventory of space use would be made periodically, probably monthly, and each crop charged with space occupied or reserved for the crop. For each inventory period, the entire production area must be completely charged to the crops. Space that is unoccupied at the time should be charged to the crop which was just removed or to the one that will follow.

After the total cost for the crop is compiled, it is divided by the number of units to get the product cost. The number of units used in this computation should be the number of units offered for sale. This figure will usually be less than the number of pots started or the number of flowers cut, and frequently it will be greater than the number of units actually sold.

Selling price may have to be based on competition, social customs, supply and demand, and governmental decree, as well as cost of product; but unless the cost of the product is known it can not be determined if the product is being sold at a profit or not. Developing cost information will require record keeping specifically for this purpose. The tax people are interested only in the total effect. It is up to management to choose the right crops, grow them correctly, price them adequately, and market them successfully so that there will be a margin between cost and selling price; and management will not be able to make the necessary decisions without product costs.

- ANALYSIS OF THE BUSINESS RECORDS SHOULD PROVIDE THE INFORMATION
  NEEDED FOR FUTURE IMPROVEMENT OF THE BUSINESS

There may have been a time when the only information needed
was that all the bills had been paid and the owner was still more
or less affluent. Regardless of the size of the business, that day is pretty
well in the past. Governmental taxing has become sufficiently formal-
ized so that each business must follow prescribed routines in reporting
and paying taxes. Because of this, business accounting procedures
have been designed through the years to provide the required information to the government first, and then additional accounting may
or may not be done to provide other information for the benefit of
management in making decisions on the operation of the business.
The magnitude of taxation has increased to the point where it has a
noticeable effect on product cost. One of the first questions management may have before making a decision is what effect will it have on
taxation.

It is not unusual for a tug-of-war to develop between owner and
accountant, in which the owner pulls for accounting decisions in favor
of the business and the accountant holds for his concept of what is
allowable under governmental regulations. Although the same regulations affect the entire country, the interpretation of them may vary from
district to district or among individuals, with the result that accounting
procedures vary. Most of the controversy is around expensing. Generally it would be favorable to the business if major expensing could
be done in years of high income and deferred in years when returns
were not so good. The regulation presumably provides that the cost
is capitalized if it can be expected to contribute to future revenues and
it is expensed if it has contributed to this year's income. Several situations arise that require judgement rulings. Yearly repairs to greenhouse
structure may be judged to be contributing primarily to current revenues and thus should be expensed yearly; but if the repairs are more
extensive it might be ruled that this is a capital improvement which
contributes to future revenues. What is the regulation on greenhouse
benches? Well, in some districts they may be expensed the year they
are built, and in others they will be considered a capital improvement.
The general ruling seems to be that plastic film houses are temporary

structures and thus expensed the year they are constructed. Glass houses are considered capital improvements, and rigid plastic houses may be expensed either way, depending on some other considerations.

There is frequent, light talk among businessmen in the area of education-convention-entertainment expenses being allowed as business expenses, and there are frequent, serious discussions between owner and his accountant on the same subject. From the standpoint of good business management, the owner should first have a frank talk with himself and decide if the expense is a wise investment for the benefit of the company. Then if it appears to be a good expenditure for the business, the next step would be to determine if it is an allowable business expense as far as the government is concerned.

When an accountant is used for analyzing the business affairs, usually one or more types of financial statements are prepared. They may be prepared purely for internal use in analyzing the business and making management decisions, or they may be used to explain the status of the firm when credit is being established or financing is sought. The balance sheet lists the assets and the liabilities—and one total does balance the other—, but some inspection and analysis of the items is needed to evaluate the status of the business. Probably the first comparison to make is current assets to current liabilities. Current assets are cash, accounts receivable, and inventory. Derivation of the value for cash should be routine in any business, but the adequacy of the methods for finding the value of accounts receivable and inventory should be determined. If the terms of business are net 30 days, what per cent of accounts receivable are over 30 days, over 60 days, and over 90 days? Inventory is not much of an item in flower- and plant-producing greenhouses; but if it is, has the method of evaluation of its worth been sound? Current liabilities include such items as notes payable, accounts payable, accrued liabilities, and reserve for taxes. Current assets must be greater than current liabilities, or financial trouble is here or impending.

The profit-and-loss or income statement lists total income less total expense, and the difference is the profit or loss. It is a summary of the distribution of the income to product costs, selling expenses, administration, interest, taxes, dividends, and retained or reinvested income.

The greenhouse operator should expect to get answers from financial statements to most of the following questions:

Is the business earning a reasonable return on the total funds he has invested?

Is the company in sound financial condition?

Are there any apparent overinvestments in fixed assets or accounts receivable?

Is the ratio of current assets to current liabilities favorable?

Does the company have sufficient working capital (current assets less current liabilities)?

Reference Reviews

1. Gordon, Myron J., and Gordon Shillinglaw, *Accounting: A Management Approach*, Fourth Edition, Richard D. Irwin, Inc., Homewood, Illinois, 1969. *This is accounting information presented for the owner or manager. The book is organized in three parts. Part 1, "Accounting Concepts and Methods," will relate directly to business procedures used in most greenhouses, and Part 2, "Measurement of Capital and Income," and Part 3, "Accounting Data for Management Planning and Control," give the methods for analyzing the business.*

2. Haynes, W. Warren, and Joseph L. Massie, *Management Analysis Concepts and Cases*, Second Edition, Prentice-Hall, Inc., Englewood Cliffs, New Jersey, 1969. *Part 4, "Analytical Tools for Decision Making," is a thorough presentation of the relationship between accounting and managerial decisions.*

3. Johnson, Robert W., *Financial Management*, Fourth Edition, Allyn & Bacon, Inc., Boston, 1971. *Part 1, "Introduction," and Part 2, "Planning and Managing Assets," give the down-to-earth financial management information that any businessman must have. The last four parts of the book are concerned primarily with external financing and would be of interest if that is involved in the business.*

4. Kennedy, Ralph Dale, and Stewart Yarwood McMullen, *Financial Statements—Form, Analysis, and Interpretation*, Third Edition, Richard D. Irwin, Inc., Homewood, Illinois, 1957. *This may be too specific a subject for many greenhouse managers, but for the ones who are interested in a better understanding of this part of the business it could be very helpful.*

5. Langhans, Robert W., et al., *Chrysanthemums—A Manual of the Culture, Diseases, Insects, and Economics of Chrysanthemums*, New York State Extension Service, Cornell University, Ithaca, 1964. *Chapter 17, "Costs,"*

discusses some of the factors of this particular product cost and reports on a survey made in New York State.

6. Laurie, Alex, D. C. Kiplinger, and Kennard S. Nelson, *Commercial Flower Forcing*, Seventh Edition, McGraw-Hill Book Company, Inc. New York, 1969. *Chapter 15, "Costs of Production," has a brief but pertinent discussion on flower and plant production costs and how they may be derived.*

7. Mastalerz, John W., et al., *Geraniums—A Manual of the Culture, Diseases, Insects, Economics, Taxonomy, and Breeding of Geraniums*, Second Edition, Pennsylvania Flower Growers, University Park, 1971. *There is excellent product cost and pricing information on geraniums in chapters 29 through 32.*

8. Mastalerz, John W., Robert W. Langhans, et al., *Roses—A Manual on the Culture, Management, Diseases, Insects, Economics, and Breeding of Greenhouse Roses*, Pennsylvania Flower Growers, University Park, New York State Flower Growers Association, Inc., Ithaca, and Roses, Inc., Haslett, Michigan, 1969. *Chapter 37, "Prices and Costs," and Chapter 38, "Prices and Competition," give some general information on costs and pricing on this specific product. Chapter 40, "Management Decision Making," contains a brief but thorough presentation of business management.*

9. Neuner, John J. W., *Cost Accounting—Principles and Practices*, Fifth Edition, Richard D. Irwin, Inc., Homewood, Illinois, 1957. *There is no reference to flower and plant products, but some of the same principles apply.*

10. Tungate, L. A., *Financial Management for the Small Businessman*, Chapman and Grimes, Inc., Boston, Massachusetts, 1952. *A very refreshing book to refer to because it relates so readily to the flower and plant business. Unfortunately the book is out of print. It may be possible to locate it in some libraries, or firms that deal in out-of-print books may have a copy available.*

CHAPTER 3

Management of the Physical
Facilities

CHAPTER 3

The physical facilities for flower and plant production in the greenhouse must be established and maintained, and this involves engineering—many kinds of engineering. Some of the basic and elementary engineering can and must be handled by the greenhouse owner or his employees. The detailed or larger engineering projects require professional help. Although most greenhouse operators are floriculturists or plantsmen who may or may not have a smattering of knowledge about engineering, there are others who may be quite adept at engineering problems and not too interested or informed on plant culture. It is a good working arrangement in a partnership or family operation when one of the individuals handles the plant culture responsibilities and the other the engineering. It is not possible here to give detailed engineering information, but it is hoped that listing the various engineering operations together with references will lead to improvement in the management of greenhouse facilities.

• THE TOOLS AND TABLES OF THE TRADE ARE NECESSARY

The greenhouse manager has to handle three hurdles before he can take care of the physical facilities—the specific information needed, the required tools, and the engineering tables. The specific information needed for the job may be obtained from schooling, a professional, a friend, or from literature, but the tools and tables must be available right on the place. Some of the tool requirements may be as simple as the need for a screw driver with a 3-inch handle instead of one 6 inches long, or the job may need some highly specialized tools designed only for that specific purpose. Tables are available for every possible engineering activity from the size, length, gauge, and number of nails per pound to wire sizes for single-phase motors. Without the proper

tools and tables the job will be botched in spite of the operator's knowing how it should be done.

Every greenhouse operation needs tools. Some may have just the
basic essentials such as hammers, saws, screwdrivers, wrenches, pipe
cutters, pipe threaders, and drills. Others may have a complete set of
all kinds of hand tools, plus machines and specialized equipment for
doing detailed work. In all instances a suitable place must be provided
for the storage of the tools and equipment together with a work area
large enough for their use, and provisions must be made for their
proper maintenance. The use, storage, and maintenance of tools must
be assigned to a responsible individual.

On any installation or in the maintenance of existing facilities,
the method of handling should be analyzed for quality of work, time
required, and costs involved. Some of the jobs that are frequently
handled by the greenhouse crew could really be done better and
cheaper by professionals in that specific trade. Major expenditures for
either equipment or maintenance should be based on bids whenever
possible, but this does not imply, however, that the lowest bid is
necessarily the best one to accept—quality and timeliness may be of
more real worth than the difference in dollars.

- **LAND GRADING, DRAINAGE, AND ROAD BUILDING
  ARE BEST LET ON CONTRACT**

This type of work requires bigger equipment than is used around
most greenhouses. The engineering firms that specialize in this work
will know what to do and have the capability of handling the work
efficiently. The point that needs to be made here is that before the
greenhouse is erected the manager should determine if the lay of
the land is suitable or if some land forming would benefit construction
work as well as future operations. If advice is needed, it may be obtained from the state extension specialist in agricultural engineering
or from professional engineering firms.

- **MINOR CONSTRUCTION AND REPAIR CAN BE HANDLED
  BY THE GREENHOUSE CREW**

At least some of the greenhouse workers should be able to do construction work; others will need considerable guidance. Occasional greenhouse operations will have qualified people to handle about any construction or repair job, but it is considered here that the local crew should not do more than fairly elementary things such as erecting benches or building a soil shed.

Even though the greenhouse manager will not get deeply involved in construction and repair work, he will want to do it well, and this can be done only if he has sufficient basic information or has a ready source of information. He must know terms and the language of the trade, units of measurement of lumber, lumber grades and uses; be able to interpret drawings and make sketches to scale; know the kinds of wood fasteners and their capabilities, be able to use the tools correctly, and have an understanding and appreciation of the value of relying on the square, level, and plumb bob.

- GOOD CONCRETE WORK REQUIRES SELECTION OF RIGHT MATERIALS, IN PROPER PROPORTIONS, THOROUGH MIXING, AND CAREFUL WORKING AND CURING

A good place to start here is with terminology. The terms *cement* and *concrete* are not synonymous. Cement is one of the ingredients of concrete. Cement plus water forms the binder which holds the aggregates (sand, crushed rock, pebbles) together. Concrete is the mixture of cement, water, and aggregates.

Cement (properly called Portland cement) is a manufactured product consisting of a mixture of limestone and clay or shale. In the manufacturing process the ingredients are ground, mixed, heated and powdered, and then the product is packaged in bags. These bags will contain one cubic foot of cement and weigh about 94 pounds. When cement is mixed with water it undergoes a chemical change and sets permanently.

Portland cement is a standard product manufactured by several companies. There are, however, different ways in which it is used in making concrete. Depending on how the concrete will be used, varying amounts of water may be added to produce concrete consistency from dry or stiff to wet and flowable. The type and size of aggregate may be varied to suit the use of the concrete. Unless the greenhouse personnel have considerable experience in concrete work, they will need help in selecting type and size of aggregate and proportions of cement, water, and aggregate to use for the job.

Concrete must be thoroughly mixed so that each particle of aggregate is coated with cement paste and the mixture is uniformly consistent, with the aggregate evenly distributed throughout the mass.

Concrete starts to set about 30 minutes after the water is added to the mixture, making it necessary to have equipment and men ready for placing the concrete in forms. Pouring and working the concrete in the forms and finishing the surface requires previous training or some advice from an experienced source. Following this, the concrete must be cured properly.

Concrete may be mixed on the site where it is to be used, or it may be brought in on ready-mixed trucks. The same quality concrete may be obtained by either method, but it may be more economical to handle it one way than the other. If ready-mixed concrete is used, it must be ordered in the exact proportions suitable for the job.

The success of concrete work also depends on the preparation of the site where the concrete will be placed. The correct depth of excavation, the proper preparation of the base, the design and strength of the forms, and the use of reinforcement or expansion joints all influence the suitability of the job. Some greenhouse operators design and build their own concrete benches. Various designs and degrees of workmanship have been used. There is no source information for such a project, and unless the greenhouse crew is knowledgeable in concrete work it would be best to have this work done by professional concrete workers.

Concrete blocks can be used in many ways around greenhouses— for walls, benches, sheds, and legs for benches. The standard concrete block is 8 inches wide, 15¾ inches long, and 7¾ inches high. If blocks are being used for bench or other supports, be sure that the workers realize that there is that ¼-inch difference between width and height so they do not place the blocks interchangeably.

● **PAINTING AND RE-GLAZING MUST BE A CONTINUOUS PROGRAM IN THE GREENHOUSE**

For wooden greenhouse structures, painting should be scheduled at two- to four-year intervals. Not only will painting help preserve the wood and reflect more light in the greenhouse, but it will help maintain the glazing in good condition for a longer period of time. If a portion of the range is repainted each year, it may be possible to do it with the greenhouse crew. Large-scale painting jobs probably should be put on bid with professionals. Any repair work to glass, bars, or structure must be handled before the painting is done. The surfaces to be painted need to be scaled and cleaned before the paint is applied. It is difficult to impress painters with the need for proper preparation of the surface before the paint is applied, yet painting will be nearly worthless when the application is made over dirt, algae, and loose, old paint. Professional painters may be as negligent in preparation as amateurs.

Most painters realize that the object is to get paint on the wood or metal to be protected, but they may not understand that the paint must be applied so that it seals the juncture of glass and wood. This requires a delicate touch, but with some coaching it can be handled by most individuals. Paint should be brushed out so that a uniformly thin coat is applied to the entire surface.

Modern greenhouse structures with aluminum bars and aluminum or galvanized steel framework do not require painting, and they eliminate considerable maintenance work.

Greenhouse workers must know how to glaze. They may not be involved in erection of new greenhouses or in complete re-glazing jobs of old ones, but there is continual repair work needed and they should be able to handle it. Glazing is required on glass houses with any type bars. It is the procedure used to seal glass to bar, making a watertight union. Broken glass will need to be replaced from time to time, and slipped glass will have to be re-set. Eventually the glazing compound deteriorates to the extent that the entire structure should be re-glazed. The life of the glazing job varies with materials, methods, climate, and some local conditions, but it should be in the vicinity of 20 years.

Greenhouses covered with materials other than glass do not require glazing, but they do need re-covering periodically. Estimates of the useful life of various coverings are less than a year for polyethylene film, one to three years for vinyl film, about five years for corrugated vinyl, and four to twenty years for fiberglass. Each of these various types of products is available in various grades, and climate differences greatly affect these materials. For these reasons there is considerable variability in the life expectancy of these coverings.

The requirements for paint and glazing compounds in the greenhouse are very specific. The needs for these supplies are best handled by firms that deal in greenhouse supplies. Paints and glazing compounds used in general construction work may not be nearly so effective as the products designed for use in the greenhouse.

● **UTILIZATION OF ELECTRICITY IN THE GREENHOUSE PROVIDES LIGHT AND HEAT AS WELL AS A MEANS OF DOING WORK AND ESTABLISHING AUTOMATION**

Although other sources of light have been used, electricity remains as the source in common usage. Electric light in the greenhouse is not only used as a means of illumination so that surroundings are visible to humans when light from the sun is not available, but for its effect on plant growth and development. There are several different types of electric lamps available, and because of constant improvement and development of new types a source of information must be used that is constantly updated. The electric company from whom the electricity is purchased should have individuals on their staff who can give reliable and timely advice on electric lamps. Incandescent (tungsten) lamps are in common usage and probably will continue to be. They are economical to install, provide acceptable light qualities, have a relatively short life, and are somewhat reasonable to operate. The highest radiation from incandescent lamps is at the red end of the spectrum. The red light is valuable for both photosynthesis and photoperiod, but the infrared (heat) radiation given off is of questionable worth in most applications. An incandescent lamp converts only about 11 per cent of the input energy to light. Flower colors appear more natural or brighter in incandescent light than they do in fluorescent light; and for this reason, in sales areas or places where flowers are displayed at least a portion of the lighting should be incandescent.

Fluorescent lamps convert about 23 per cent of the input energy into light and because of this are more economical to operate than incandescent lamps. They can be expected to have a longer life than incandescent lamps, but the installation costs are higher. Various types of fluorescent lamps are available, and some of them may be used effectively for office or workroom lighting and plant growth chambers, and for regulation of photoperiod. The best source for advice on the use of fluorescent lamps should be the company that supplies the electricity.

Mercury vapor lamps, and more recently metal-halide lamps, may have some application for use in the greenhouse. The installation costs are relatively high, but these lamps have a high efficiency (conversion of input energy into light is greater than either incandescent or fluorescent lamps) and a long life expectancy. The metal-halide lamps have certain advantages over the mercury lamps, and it appears that their use will increase. The metal-halide lamps may have application in illuminating large areas such as workrooms or in greenhouses for supplementing daylight.

Illumination may be expressed in various terms. In the greenhouse it is most common to refer to foot-candles, and determinations are made with a meter calibrated in those units (not a photographer's meter). A foot-candle meter can be obtained from firms that handle greenhouse supplies, or it may be possible to borrow one from the electric company. There should be frequent need for a light meter around a greenhouse, however, and the manager should have one available for use when he needs it. Lamp manufacturers may rate lamps in lumens, and one lumen per square foot equals the illumination received by a surface every point of which is distant one foot from a source of one candle power. Actually there is considerable difference of opinion and controversy over methods of light measurement. There are sound reasons for the various methods, but until equipment and procedures are developed for commercial use the greenhouse manager should use the foot-candle meters and express light intensities in terms of foot-candles.

Some foot-candle values that pertain to the greenhouse area are: at Columbus, Ohio, for example, at noon on a clear summer day, 10,000 plus foot-candles, and at noon on an overcast day in December, 100 foot-candles; plant growth chamber with electric lights as sole source of light, 2,000 to 4,000 foot-candles for 16-hour day; potting room, 50 to

100 foot-candles; office, 100 to 200 foot-candles; and photoperiod light-ing, 10 foot-candles. The light evaluation must be made at the plant level or the position at which the work is being done. Recommendations for kind, size, and placement of lamps for office, warehouse, or potting room can be obtained from the electric company. The method for using lights to promote photosynthesis or regulate photoperiodism is in Chap-ter 6.

Electric lights are rated in watts so the energy input to each light is known. Electric current is metered as kilowatt-hours. To determine the cost of electricity for lighting an area, total the watts for the lamps that will be used, divide by 1,000 (there are 1,000 watts per kilowatt), multiply by the number of hours they will be in use, and then multiply by the rate per kilowatt-hour. To determine the cost of electric current each night for lighting a 100-foot bench of chrysanthemums in which 60-watt lamps are spaced 4 feet apart and 2 feet above the plants (25 lamps), and a rate of .02 per kilowatt-hour, the computation would

be: $\dfrac{(25 \times 60)}{1,000} \times 4 \times .02 = .12$ Actually this may be a simplifica-

tion, because rates vary and may be based on the time of use, peak load, and other factors. The electric company involved would be able to discuss all the various possibilities.

Electric current is transported in a suitable conductor. The most familiar conductor is copper wire. As might be expected, a large diam-eter wire is required for transporting a large flow of electric current. The term for unit flow of electricity is ampere (1 ampere equals a flow of 6.25 billion, billion electrons per second). Some electrical appliances have the ampere requirement for operation listed on them; but as noted earlier, electric lamps have only a watt rating. Because watts equal amperes times volts, the ampere requirement per lamp can be determined by dividing the watts by the volts. Using the same chrysan-

themum bench as previously, the computation would be $\dfrac{25 \times 60}{115}$

or approximately 13 amperes current required for lighting that 100-foot bench of mums. Standard tables list the safe carrying capacity of insulated copper wire as being 15 amperes for #14 wire and 20 amperes for #12 wire. Although it is indicated that #14 wire could be used, #12 wire probably would be chosen for extra safety.

In the United States electric alternating current is 60-cycle. In Europe 50-cycle current is used, and in Canada many areas changed from 50-cycle to 60-cycle rather recently. Electric current may be transported at various voltages(pressures). Around the home and greenhouse the most common voltages in use are 115-volt and 230-volt. Lights, small appliances, and small motors are usually on 115-volt and stoves and large motors on 230-volt current. It is possible to use 230-volt current for electric lights, but 230-volt lamps would have to be used. If 230-volt current had been used in the preceding example, the flow of amperes would have been cut in half because the total watts (1,500) divided by the volts (230) equals the amperes (about 6.5). Because of the lower amperage, smaller wire can be used. In this example #14 wire probably would be used.

Electricity is not used as a general source of heat in the greenhouse, but it is frequently used for propagation areas. Higher than normal temperatures are required for propagation, and the control must be exact. Electric soil-heating cable with thermostat is designed for such a purpose, and it is available in either 115-volt or 230-volt. The cost of equipment would be about $1 per square foot, with small areas running something more and large areas considerably less. Soil-heating cable is rated in watts and amperes. A standard 60-foot cable is 400 watts and 3.33 amperes, and each cable would be distributed over an area of 36 square feet. Three cables would handle a 100-square foot area, and they could be regulated by the standard thermostat assembly rated at 15 amperes—in fact this thermostat could handle a fourth cable if additional area needed to be heated. With the three cables in this 100-square foot area in service, 1,200-watts (1.2 kilowatts) of power would be used. If the cost of current is 2 cents per kilowatt hour, the cost of heating the 100 square feet for each hour the current is on would be about 2½ cents. The 115-volt cable and thermostats are designed for plugging directly into standard electric outlets. The 230-volt thermostat assembly must be wired on the job, so the services of an electrician will be required for that installation.

There are many different types of electric motors, and they all are used to convert electric energy to movement. Electric motors are designed around the basic fact that there is a magnetic field adjacent to a conductor (wire) carrying an electric current, and if the conductor is coiled around a metal core, it is possible to make an electromagnet. Because opposite poles of a magnet attract and like poles repel, it is possible to produce movement with certain arrangements of electromagnets. Various clever and intricate means are used for making electric motors of many different sizes, capabilities, and designs. The selection, installation, and use of electric motors is a specialized field, and the advice and service of qualified professionals are needed. It should be realized that there are various levels of training and understanding among electricians, and some of them know motors and their use and others do not. Many items of electrical equipment are supplied with proper motors by the manufacturer, but they will need to be connected correctly when the equipment is installed. This is a job for the professional motor man.

Electric motors have name plates on them, and the user should know the significance of the information listed here. The manufacturer's name is on the plate, and the model number and serial number of the motor. By referring to the model number and serial number, any information needed about the motor may be obtained from the manufacturer. Motors are warranted by manufacturers, and if the motor malfunctions within the warranty period a replacement or an adjustment may be obtained from the manufacturer's local agent. Warranties on electric motors are directly between customer and motor manufacturer—similar to the way tire and battery warranties are handled on automobiles.

The nameplate will specify the kind of current the motor can be connected to. Most of the motors around the greenhouse will use alternating current (AC) and 60-cycle. Smaller-capacity motors are designed to use one-phase current, either 115-volt or 230-volt. Larger-capacity motors usually are 230-volt and may be either one-phase or three-phase. Wiring instructions for the motor may be on the nameplate, or they may be on an attached tag or instruction leaflet. The electrician needs this information in order to make the right connections to the motor.

The size motor or the amount of work it will do is indicated in horsepower (hp). One horsepower is equivalent to about 746 watts; but for practical purposes, because of electrical energy losses to friction and heat, about 1,000 watts (one kilowatt) of electrical energy must be supplied to the motor to produce one hp of mechanical energy. More current is required to start a motor than to keep it operating. Depending on the type of motor, the current to start it may be two to eight times as great as the operating current. This must be considered in choosing service wires and fuses for motors. The amperage requirement for the rated horsepower is indicated on the nameplate. If it is a dual-voltage motor, the first figure (larger) refers to the lower voltage and the second figure (smaller) is for the higher voltage.

In normal operation the motor temperature increases. The amount of temperature rise to be expected is indicated on the nameplate in degrees Centigrade. If the motor exceeds that temperature rise the cause could be connection to a wrong circuit, too heavy a load on the motor, lack of air circulation around the motor, moisture or dirt in the motor, or operation at high altitudes or in a hot environment.

Motors must be kept free from moisture and dirt, and they may or may not require oiling. The oiling needs should be specified on the nameplate or on a tag or leaflet attached to the motor. Some motors have permanently sealed bearings that require no addition of oil. Others should be oiled periodically. The recommendations for grade of oil, frequency of oiling, and amount of oil to be applied should be followed very carefully.

Greenhouse managers should have a good general understanding of electricity. They should be able to figure current demand for the lights and equipment that are in use and be able to determine if conductors (wires), switches, and fuses are adequate for the demand. Electrical installations, however simple they may seem to be, should be handled by qualified electricians. Electrical work improperly done may lead to destruction of equipment, to fires, or to electrocution.

Some of the circuits used in the greenhouse are 24-volt. These are situations in which the current demand is low, but danger to personnel is possible. Some of the most common 24-volt usage is for timers and electric water valves.

Getting the power from the motor to the point where the work will be done may involve a direct connection between motor and machine (direct drive), gears, or belts. Many of the applications in the greenhouse are with V-belts, and the belts transfer the power from the pulley wheel of the motor to the pulley wheel of the machine to be operated. If the same-size pulley is used on machine and motor, the shaft of the machine will revolve at the same rate as the motor shaft. If the machine pulley is half the diameter of the motor pulley, the machine pulley will operate at twice the speed of the motor pulley (the diameter of one pulley multiplied by its speed is equal to the diameter of the other pulley multiplied by its speed). The speed (rpm) of the motor is listed on the nameplate of the motor, and the diameter of the pulley can be measured. The manufacturer of the machine either specifies the speed at which it is to be operated, or lists the size motor, motor speed, and motor pulley diameter to be used with the machine. The shafts of motor and machine must be parallel so that the belt runs at a 90-degree angle to them.

V-belts are measured by width, depth, and outer circumference; and when a belt is replaced it should be with one of the same size. The means of replacing one varies with the motor or machine, but there will be a way to make adjustment between the two to regulate the tension on the belt. The belt should have some slack in it.

Electricity is used for many of the vital operations in the greenhouse, and a cessation of service for any length of time can be disastrous. All greenhouses need their own stand-by generator to handle such emergencies. The generator must be large enough to operate the heating system, pump water, run refrigerators, and operate ventilation, as well as provide enough light. In selecting the size generator to handle these needs, it must be kept in mind that motors will usually have to be started as well as operated and the power demand for starting motors may be considerably greater. If the emergency power is minimal, care must be taken to start the various systems in rotation, so that the entire starting load does not come at the same time.

The cost for an entirely automatic stand-by power generator may be about twice the cost of a manual unit. In most instances a manual-start generator is satisfactory in the greenhouse because either there is some personnel around at all times or there is an adequate warning system to bring the operator. A routine must be established to keep the generator in operating condition. It needs to be started and operated long enough once a week or at least monthly to make certain that it will deliver the necessary power during an emergency.

- IT REQUIRES GREAT QUANTITIES OF GOOD WATER TO SUPPLY THE PLANTS AS WELL AS KEEP THE GREENHOUSE OPERATING

Plants are 85 per cent or so water, and in the greenhouse the water must be supplied to the plants. Plants grown outdoors receive all or possibly most of their water from rainfall, but the greenhouse plants must be irrigated. A considerable portion of the water that enters plants is lost from them via transpiration, so the water requirements for plants are much greater than the volume retained by the plant. Other water requirements around the greenhouse are make-up water for the boiler, for moistening the pads in fan and pad-cooling systems, for use by personnel, for hydraulic spraying, and for clean-up work.

The quantity of water needed for the entire operation must be determined so that an adequate source can be located and the distribution pipe sizes calculated to handle that flow of water. If water from the municipal water system is available, it probably is the best source of supply and should be used. The other water sources would be those developed locally, such as wells or ponds. If there is any question about the ability of the water source to supply the volume needed, provisions must be made for an alternate source of supply. Water flow in pipes may be referred to as gallons per minute (gpm) or as cubic feet per minute (cfm). One gallon equals .134 cubic feet. The rate of flow of water in pipes is dependent on the size pipe, the water pressure, the length of pipe, the kind of material of which the pipe is made, the kind and number of fittings used on the pipe, the condition of the pipe, and any restriction to the flow at the discharge end. There is some friction between water and the wall of the pipe, and this reduces the water pressure and the rate of flow. The longer the run of pipe, the greater the drop in pressure and flow. There is considerably less friction loss (about one-third less) in plastic pipe than in iron. There are so many variables that it is not possible to give exact rates of water delivery from pipe, but the following values for various sizes of iron pipe at two different lengths (35 feet and 100 feet), with water at 40-pound pressure per square inch (psi), are realistic: ¾ inch— 26 gpm and 16 gpm; 1 inch—53 gpm and 33 gpm; 1½ inches—143 gpm and 90 gpm; 2 inches—287 gpm and 184 gpm; 3 inches—760 gpm and 501 gpm; and 4 inches—1,498 gpm and 1,018 gpm. The two points of interest here are the great increase in rate of water flow that is possible by using the next larger size of pipe, and great reduction in rate of flow with increased pipe length.

Water quality is highly important in the greenhouse. Few if any available water sources offer pure water—the water has some materials dissolved or suspended in it. If it is from a municipal system, it may be expected to be potable, and it should not have materials suspended in it. The quantities of substances dissolved in it vary, depending on the source of the water and how it is treated before it is dispensed into the water mains. There is no indication that chlorination of water has any bad effects on plants. Some municipalities have facilities for removing some of the dissolved substance, and in general this will make the water suitable for use in the greenhouse.

When a municipal source of water cannot be used, the greenhouse operator must develop his own source, and here both quantity and quality of water may be a problem. Wells are the most common local source of water. If one does not supply enough water, another one is developed. Well water varies considerably in quality; and because it is not feasible to establish a treatment system, the water is used as is or the well is abandoned. The most common problem with well water is the great amount of dissolved substances in it—primarily calcium and magnesium compounds, and possibly iron. Such water must be treated for boiler use. It may be used satisfactorily for irrigation with the exception that the irrigation equipment may become corroded and eventually plugged. Wherever this kind of water evaporates it leaves a residue, so if it is used for misting or syringing, the plants become covered with the residue and some types of nozzles will plug. Pads in fan and pad systems will become encrusted with salts, and probably plugged.

It is possible to pump silt or sand along with the water from some wells. It may be possible to remove the sand by filter, but silt is very hard to eliminate. Sand or silt is very abrasive to water pumps and fertilizer injectors, creating undue wear and early replacement of equipment.

Well work is a job for a professional and it should be contracted with complete understanding of terms.

Ponds may be a good source of water for the greenhouse. This water will not be potable and a separate water supply for personnel use will need to be used. Pond water usually does not have a high quantity of substances dissolved in it, but it probably will have an oversupply of material suspended in it. Silt and algae in pond water are common, and it is difficult to filter either one. The better approach is to eliminate them at the source. Expert advice is needed for the construction and management of a pond.

The general concept is that soft water contains much less dissolved minerals than hard water. This probably is true for natural water supplies, but it is not so for hard water that has been softened by some of the most common commercial or home procedures. As mentioned previously, hard water contains calcium, magnesium, and possibly iron compounds, and the common softening procedures merely replace these materials with sodium compounds which may leave as much residue and corrosion around the greenhouse in spite of being classed as soft water. The procedures which could be used to make water soft by actually removing the chemicals from the water are either too laborious or costly to be used on greenhouse water.

The pH of water may be of some concern. There have been reports of pH from 8.0 to 10.0 with possible adverse effects on plant growth. It should be possible to make adjustment for this high pH by using more acid fertilizers in the soil—using ammonium nitrate instead of sodium or calcium nitrate or making applications of iron sulfate or sulfur to the soil. If this does not seem to be effective, it may be necessary to inject phosphoric acid into the irrigation water.

The question sometimes arises as to whether the water source has too many salts dissolved in it. This may be evaluated with the Solu Bridge. Using model RDB-15 values below 2.00 should be satisfactory.

The greenhouse operator needs to be some kind of expert at working with pipe. He should hire a plumber to install a toilet, but he should know how to cut pipe, thread it, and install any part of the distribution system for irrigation. He must also know how much water will be required for each installation and how that demand can be met. If an irrigation system is being installed, the water delivery per nozzle or tube needs to be known so that the total demand for the system can be figured. The manufacturer of the equipment can supply this information, or the water flow can be metered. The meter reading may be made at the main meter if there is no other demand for water during the time the reading is being made. If this is not possible, a meter could be borrowed from the water company and placed directly in the irrigation supply line. The water meters will probably give values in cubic feet; but as noted earlier, one gallon equals about .134 cubic foot. The meter reading should be observed at the start of the trial, the system turned on, and the reading noted after five minutes. The original reading should be subtracted from the final reading and divided by 5; this value will be the number of cubic feet of water used by the system per minute. When that is divided by .134, the water flow rate then will be in terms of gallons per minute.

There are some situations in which plastic pipe can be used to advantage in the greenhouse. Polyethylene pipe is relatively inexpensive, but for certain purposes it may be used very satisfactorily. It is flexible and is shipped in 100-foot or 400-foot rolls. It is black in color, and the 80-pound pipe is the common grade used in the greenhouse. Because it is flexible it needs continuous support, such as installing on top the bench side board or on the soil surface. Polyethylene pipe lengthens with increase in temperature, and if it is positioned in a straight line during cool temperatures, it will snake in warmer temperatures. For this reason polyethylene pipe should be installed in warm temperatures, stretched, and then both ends fastened. Nozzle installations should be made after the poly pipe is in place on the bench, for best alignment of nozzle. Fittings for poly pipe are insert type—the knurled end rams into the pipe. For connection directly to iron pipe, a fitting is used with a knurled end for the poly pipe and with iron pipe threads for the other end. For temporary connection, a female hose coupling may be installed directly in the poly pipe so that a hose may be attached, or an insert coupling may be used with one insert in the pipe and the other in a length of water hose with a female hose coupling on it. Insert fittings give a snug fit in the pipe, and it may not be necessary to use clamps. This will depend on the water pressure and the manner in which the system is to be used. The internal diameter (ID) of polyethylene pipe is nominally the same diameter as iron pipe.

Polyvinyl chloride (PVC) pipe is semi-rigid and gray in color, and is in 20-foot lengths. There are two grades (weights) of PVC pipe used in the greenhouse—200-pound and schedule 40. Schedule 40 PVC pipe has a heavier wall than 200-pound pipe, and it is more rigid. However, it is not nearly so rigid as iron pipe. PVC fittings are designed to slip over the outside of the pipe, and for this reason the outer diameter (OD) of PVC pipe is the same regardless of grade. The lighter weight pipe (200-pound) has a greater ID than schedule 40 pipe and has a greater potential water flow rate. The nominal ID of schedule 40 PVC pipe is about the same as the ID for polyethylene and iron pipe. For attachment directly to iron pipe, fittings are used with slip for the PVC side and iron pipe threads for the other. PVC fittings are usually put on with an adhesive which makes the bond permanent. For temporary attachment of water line to PVC pipe it might be best to terminate the pipe with female iron pipe threads and use an insert fitting male adapter in it. A length of water hose could then be rammed over the knurled end of the adapter. Schedule 40 PVC pipe costs about twice as much as polyethylene pipe and 200-pound PVC pipe about half again as much as poly pipe, but their semi-rigid property is of real value in some cases. Small, self-tapping nozzles may be used in either poly or 200-pound PVC pipe, but schedule 40 pipe must be used if threads must be tapped into the pipe. It is possible to use schedule 40 PVC pipe for misting lines, but more support will be required than with iron pipe.

With most irrigation and misting systems it is desired that the distribution of water be uniform, and that it start and stop at the same time, the entire length of the bench. For this to occur the lines must be level and the valve that controls the water must be at that same level or below it. For most uniform water distribution, the water should be introduced to the irrigation system from the middle.

Uniformity of irrigation with the small-diameter poly tube system for pot plants is dependent on having long enough tubes to the pots and having the same length tubes to each pot in the system. If the tubes are too short, the pots at the water inlet end will receive more water than those at the opposite end. If the tubes on the same bench are of different lengths, the pots serviced with short tubes will receive more water than those with longer ones.

If misting or irrigation systems are to be automated, valves operated by timers will be required. These most frequently are electric equipment. For misting systems, the electric water valve should be the piston type, as they are designed for the short contact period used in misting. A strainer should be provided on the water inlet side of the valve. For irrigation systems, diaphragm-type valves are satisfactory. In either instance the coils (solenoids) must be waterproof, and the valve certainly should be bought on performance rather than initial cost. A good electric water valve will give trouble-free service for years.

The electric water valves are controlled by clocks or timers. The objective with the misting system is to maintain a film of moisture on the leaves until roots start to form, and this requires a short burst (three to five seconds) of mist about every minute. As rooting occurs the mist is supplied less frequently—possibly once every three minutes, then five minutes, then 10 minutes, and possibly 30 minutes or longer, toward the end of propagation. There will probably be a day-night clock in the circuit so that the system may be activated for the desired period each 24 hours. It is usually considered that misting systems are operated during the daytime and are off at night. This is the best procedure during warm weather, but some thought should be given to operation during the night when outdoor temperatures are cold, because the greenhouse air may be quite dry then. Misting systems require small volumes of water, and there should be no problem in meeting the water demand.

Making the electrical connection for timer and valve is not involved and should be handled easily by any electrician. Many timers have five terminals, and there are wiring instructions with each unit. Two of the terminals are designed for the power supply; and when this connection is made, current will be supplied to the motor, which rotates the timer dial. But without further connections there will be no other response. The other three terminals are for the switch (microswitch), but only two of them are used at a time—the alternate terminal gives the opposite response. If the wiring instructions on the timer are followed there will be no problem, but if the power lines are connected directly to the switch terminals the switch will be burned out.

The situation with irrigation systems is quite different. The contact period needs to be in the vicinity of 5 to 10 minutes, and the frequency varying with crop and weather from twice a day to once every several days. The timer for irrigation must be considerably more sophisticated than the misting timer in order to provide for the variables. The following information must be on hand in order to select the correct type of irrigation timer: (1) total rate of water flow available for the entire greenhouse; (2) total number of areas to be irrigated; (3) water flow rate for each of these areas; (4) minimum and maximum irrigation time for each area; and (5) physical relationship of the various areas. If the water demand for one or more of the areas is the same as the available water flow rate for the entire greenhouse, then the irrigation must be coordinated so that those areas are not irrigated at the same time. If the total number of areas is not too great or the length of irrigation time too different, the best solution probably would be to use one timer to control the irrigation for the entire range. Pots require a shorter irrigation time than cut flowers, and because these crops are usually segregated physically, too, it is generally best to have separate timers for pot and cut flower crops. There is an advantage in having the timer centrally located to the areas controlled by it because that provides the minimum length of wire from timer to valves and it puts the timer in the vicinity of the personnel who will be using it.

It is suggested that 24-volt equipment be chosen for irrigation timers and electric water valves. The amperage required for timers and valves is so low that wiring can be done with bell wire in spite of the low voltage, and the 24-volt circuit gives maximum safety for personnel. Running the wire and making the connection between valve and timer is not difficult and could be handled by someone on the greenhouse crew with some knowledge of electrical hook-ups. The irrigation timers, however, are involved, and repair or adjustment probably should be handled by the manufacturer.

• THE GREENHOUSE MANAGER MUST BE A STATIONARY ENGINEER

Well, he may not have to be a stationary engineer, but it certainly is a big help if he is. Heating is a big part of the greenhouse business, and it does need good management. The best place to start is with fuels, because the choice of fuel will dictate the means of combustion. A few years ago coal was the accepted fuel. Various grades were used, depending on location in relation to mines. The use of coal has decreased because of the price increase per Btu value; occasional problems in getting delivery when required; a materials-handling problem in getting coal from storage area into combustion chamber and ashes from the combustion chamber to disposal area; the time lag in starting or stopping the heating cycle; clean-up time involved in removing unburned residues from equipment; and the discharge of unburned residues into the air.

In evaluating fuel costs the Btu value of the fuel is important, but other factors contributing to the cost must be considered. If the cost per Btu is higher for gas, what savings can be effected by reduced materials handling, time lag elimination, and cleanliness of equipment and environment? If gas is apparently advantageous in this respect, of what worth is it if delivery cannot be guaranteed at all times? Oil may present a few more maintenance problems than gas, but does it have other advantages? Fuel must be evaluated on a local basis, and it may have to be reevaluated from time to time, with changes in availability, regulations, equipment, and pricing.

There are some incidental uses in which the heat of fuel combustion is transferred to air and the hot air distributed around the greenhouse. There is not a practical way to transport quantities of heated air for any distance, so a hot air system would involve relatively small combustion units spaced throughout the greenhouse area. It is difficult to get uniform distribution of heat with such units. For a small operation such an installation might be more economical than a central heating system, but for a range of any size the installation, operating, and maintenance costs could very well be greater. The fuel for unit heaters usually is gas, and they should be vented to the exterior and an adequate air duct for each unit provided. Although they are fairly trouble-free, it is worthwhile to get units that can be serviced promptly and efficiently locally.

Most greenhouses use central heating systems in which the heat of fuel combustion is transferred to water and the heat distributed throughout the greenhouse area as steam or hot water. Steam systems are used more commonly in the United States, but hot water can be used very satisfactorily. If a hot water system is installed, provisions should be made for a source of steam for soil treatment. Possibly the hot water boiler can be converted to steam when needed, or a steam boiler may be installed solely for steaming soil. The size and number of units for generating heat will depend on the heat requirements for the entire range. The amount of heat required to maintain the necessary temperatures in the greenhouse must be computed first before a decision can be made on amount of heating equipment. It is wise to use two or more heat-generating units, each one capable of maintaining minimum temperatures for the entire range. Thus if one unit fails, the other could be depended on to maintain growing temperatures in usual weather conditions or to prevent freezing in severe conditions. To determine the heat requirement for the greenhouse, it must be known what temperature is to be maintained inside at the coldest expected temperature outdoors. If it is desired to maintain 60°F. indoors when it is −10°F. outdoors, the temperature difference to be maintained is 70°F. Heat is lost from the greenhouse directly through the covering as well as through any openings to the exterior that there might be in this covering. To figure the loss of heat directly through the greenhouse covering, the total amount of exposed surface to the exterior must be known. This is a routine computation. The amount of heat loss by infiltration through openings to the exterior varies. Some of the factors involved are the amount of area in glass laps, how much glass is out or cracked, the extent to which the site is exposed so that wind is a considerable factor, and the wind velocity. Because of these imponderables, it is considered sensible to estimate the heat loss via infiltration on the basis of the probable number of air changes per hour.

In a sound structure in average conditions the air changes in a glass greenhouse per hour probably would be about two changes per hour. In a plastic-covered greenhouse the air changes per hour should be less, and in an older greenhouse or in areas or conditions with considerable wind, the changes per hour would be more. To know how much air is involved in this change, the cubic contents of the greenhouse must be computed—length × width × height. There is no problem with length and width, but it is probably best to take height in two jags. First, the volume of the greenhouse to the eave or gutter must be figured— length × width × height of side wall–, and then the volume above the eave or gutter. If the greenhouse is standard pitch (6-inch rise per foot), the height of the ridge above the eave will be one-fourth the width of the house. With that dimension known, the volume above the eave is length × width × height above the ridge divided by 2. The total cubic contents of the greenhouse can be arrived at by adding the volume below the eave to the volume above the eave. For a greenhouse 40 feet wide and 200 feet long, with standard roof pitch and 7-foot side walls, the computation is:

$$40 \times 200 \times 7 = 56,000 \text{ cubic feet below eave}$$
$$\tfrac{1}{4} \times 40 = 10\text{-foot ridge above eave}$$
$$\frac{40 \times 200 \times 10}{2} = 40,000 \text{ cubic feet above eave}$$
$$56,000 + 40,000 = 96,000 \text{ cubic feet—total volume of greenhouse}$$

Assuming that the air infiltration in this house would be two changes per hour, 192,000 cubic feet (96,000 × 2) of air would be involved. Approximately 0.02 Btu is required to raise the temperature of one cubic foot of air 1°F. With this greenhouse, to maintain a temperature of 60°F. indoors at −10°F. (a 70°F. differential), about 268,000 Btu per hour (192,000 × .02 × 70) would be required to replace the heat lost by infiltration.

Most of the heat loss in the greenhouse is directly by conduction through the greenhouse covering, and the rate of loss depends on the temperature differential between inside and outside the covering. The greatest heat loss is through the roof, because this is the greatest area exposed, and the temperature differential is also greatest there. The rate of heat conduction varies with the material—it is slower through a concrete wall than through glass but about the same through transite as it is through glass. The heat transmission coefficient for glass is about 1.13, and that of concrete and wood is one-half that. The greenhouse in the previous example has 3-foot concrete side walls, and in figuring the total exposed area the concrete wall area will be divided in half for the computation. The area of the roof is obtained by multiplying the length of the roof bar by the length of the house and multiplying by two. If the length of the roof bar is not known, it may be computed from values which are known. The length of the roof bar is the square root of the sum of the squares of the other sides of the triangle formed by the roof bar, half the width of the house, and the height from eave to ridge. For the same house used previously, the calculation would be: length of roof bar $= \sqrt{(20^2) + (10^2)} = \sqrt{(20 \times 20) + (10 \times 10)} = \sqrt{500} = 22.4$ feet. The area of the roof then is $22.4 \times 2 \times 200 = 8,960$ square feet. The area of the side walls is determined in area equivalent to glass. The 7-foot walls are 4-foot glass and 3-foot concrete, with coefficient of heat transfer about one-half that of glass; thus the computation is: area of side walls in glass equivalent $= (4 + \frac{3}{2}) \times 200 \times 2 = 5.5 \times 200 \times 2 = 2,200$ square feet. The area in the gable ends below the eave is figured in the same way— $(4 + \frac{3}{2}) \times 40 \times 2 = 440$ square feet. To figure the area in the gable ends above the eave, the width of the house and the height from eave to ridge is used. For one gable end, that would be $\dfrac{40 \times 10}{2} = 200$ square feet, but for the two gable ends it is $\dfrac{(40 \times 10)}{2} \times 2 = 400$ square feet.

The entire exposed area of the greenhouse is the sum of the roof area (8,960 square feet), side wall area (2,200 square feet), and the gable end areas (440 + 400) square feet—$8,960 + 2,200 + 840 = 12,000$ square feet.

To figure the heat loss in Btu per hour through the greenhouse covering, the exposed area (12,000) is multiplied by the heat transmission coefficient through glass (1.13), and that product is multiplied by the temperature differential $(70)-12,000 \times 1.13 \times 70 = 949,200$ Btu per hour. The total loss in heat from this greenhouse by infiltration through openings (268,800 Btu) and by conduction through the greenhouse covering (949,200 Btu) is 1,218,000 Btu per hour.

One pound of steam produces about 970 Btu. At the maximum demand (60°F. inside at −10°F. outdoors) it would require about 1,256 pounds of steam (1,218,000 ÷ 970) at the greenhouse. The capacity of the boiler would have to be greater than that, however, in order to take care of the heat lost in transmission to the greenhouse. The heat loss may be in the order of one-third to one-half. For the lower value, the boiler requirement would be about 1,875 pounds of steam per hour; but if the heat loss was one-half, the boiler would have to supply about 2,512 pounds of steam per hour.

Boiler output is rated in various terms, depending on manufacturer and area of the country. A boiler rated in horse power (hp) could be expected to produce about 33,475 Btu per hour per hp. With very little heat loss, this greenhouse would require a 40-hp boiler; or with one-half the heat lost in transmission, the requirement would be about an 80-hp boiler.

As mentioned previously, it is good insurance to provide dual heat generation facilities for the greenhouse. In this instance two boilers would be installed, each with about 1,400 pounds per hour steam capacity; thus either boiler could be used in mild weather, and both boilers could be used to carry the load in cold weather.

Selection and installation of the boiler requires some professional help. It may be possible to use local heating specialists if their equipment, service, and advice are reliable. Regardless of where the unit is purchased, it should be determined at that time whether replacement parts and service will be immediately available as needed during operation. Many local boiler supply firms will not have had actual experience in greenhouse heating, and may not know how to figure heat demand or installation of heating lines in the greenhouse. For expert help in planning and installing the entire heating system, it is necessary to deal with the greenhouse construction people as they also specialize in heating equipment for greenhouses.

Depending on the size and type of boiler, and way in which it will be used, a licensed operator may or may not be required to be on duty during the operation of the boiler. Even if a licensed operator is not required, the greenhouse manager or someone in his employ must fully understand how to operate the heating system. Most boilers are controlled electrically. The operation is automatic and theoretically will proceed on its own; but some human being must know the workings of the equipment, check periodically for malfunction, and be able to take the necessary action as needed. There will be some functions that will need to be done routinely, and this will vary with the type of equipment. Boiler water must be carefully monitored to verify that the amount is sufficient. It will also need to be tested regularly and treated to prevent corrosion of boiler and lines. Both steam and hot water systems operate essentially as closed systems. The same water is continuously recirculated, and during normal heating procedures a great amount of make-up water is not required. Water lost from the system because of leaks in pipes will have to be replaced, and of course in steaming soil considerable water is lost from the heating system and will have to be replaced.

The heat is transferred from the boiler to the greenhouses with the hot water or the steam flowing in large pipes (mains) to the various greenhouses in the range. The natural flow as affected by gravity is the upward movement of the hot (and lighter) steam or water and the downward movement of the cool (and heavier) water. If the boiler is on a lower level than the greenhouse, it is possible to transport the heat solely by the effect of gravity. In many instances it is more practical to move heat by mechanical means as well as by the effect of gravity. Motor-driven accelerators or circulators are used for hot water systems and pumps for steam. Steam mains are pitched up so that any water that collects in the main will flow back toward the boiler. Steam may be produced in the boiler and transported to the greenhouses at relatively high pressure (15 to 90 psi). Then at each greenhouse a reducing valve is used to drop the pressure to 5 psi or less, for circulation in the heating lines.

Heat from steam and hot water systems is distributed in the greenhouse by means of iron pipes located to give as uniform as possible heating throughout the greenhouse. The planning and installation of the heating lines may be done by a greenhouse construction firm, or it may be done by the greenhouse operator. It should be expected that the greenhouse manager will be able to figure heat demand in the greenhouse and plan the placement of heating lines, and the greenhouse crew should be able to make the installation. If the crew does not put in the original heating lines, certainly they will get involved eventually in replacing pipe as needed. With hot water, 2-inch heating lines are commonly used; and with 180°F. water in a 60°F. house, they would produce about 160 Btu per lineal foot of pipe. With steam in the heating lines at about one pound psi (215°F.), 1¼-inch pipe gives off about 180-Btu per hour in a 60°F. greenhouse. As the steam flows through the heating lines, the loss of heat to the surroundings causes it to condense to water. It is important that this water (condensate) flow naturally (effect of gravity) toward the return lines. The steam heating line must be pitched downward from one to 2 inches per 100 feet of pipe to promote the natural flow of condensate. Steam heating lines terminate with traps which allow the passage of condensate to the return pipe but block the flow of steam. The condensate return lines must be pitched (one to 2 inches per lineal foot) downward toward the condensate return pump.

The heat requirement for the greenhouse discussed earlier was 1,218,000 Btu per hour. With a steam system and using 1¼-inch heating lines, it would require about 6,800 lineal feet (1,218,000 ÷ 180) of heating lines. At least one-fourth of the total heat should be supplied at the walls. With six heating lines on side walls and ends, that would be 2,880 lineal feet of line. If the house had seven benches, with a heating line around each bench and a line above each bench, that would provide about 4,200 lineal feet of heating lines. The exact arrangement of heating lines would depend on the design of the house and the location of the steam main and condensate return pipe. For the usual steam pressure carried in heating lines, up to 750 feet of 1¼-inch heating line can be used before trapping. In this instance it might be most practical to use a down and back arrangement in the 200-foot house, or heating lines of approximately 400 feet.

The heating lines need to be valved so that they may be controlled to correspond with the variable temperature demands. There usually are some advantages in having manual valves on each heating line even if the entire house is on automatic controls. Standard operating procedure would be to use the side heating lines at first call for heat, followed by the overhead heating lines and then the bench heating lines, as more heat is required. It may be possible to provide this control of heating manually, by a manual and automatic combination, or entirely automatically. Some degree of automation seems to be essential, but completely automatic controls may be more costly than the increase in control warrants.

Routine maintenance of steam heating lines involves repair or replacement of leaking pipe and repair or replacement of steam traps. If the trap does not pass water, the heating line fills with water, steam cannot enter the line, and it is non-functional. A heating line that is cold, in spite of being valved for steam, is the symptom of trap trouble. If the trap malfunction allows the passage of both steam and water, the condensate return line in that vicinity obviously will be hotter than should be expected.

- **REDUCING GREENHOUSE TEMPERATURES DURING COOL WEATHER IS HANDLED BY EXCHANGE OF AIR WITH OUTDOORS**

Temperature control in the greenhouse must be exact. The neophyte is inclined to believe that the only temperature problem in the greenhouse is to keep it warm enough—someplace above freezing. The greenhouse manager soon learns that too warm temperatures are nearly as bad for plants as temperatures which are too cold. The desired plant growth and development occur only within a very narrow temperature range. Because of this it is necessary to add heat or remove it promptly as needed.

During cool weather the problem is somewhat elementary. It is just a matter of exchanging greenhouse air with outdoors air—in the right proportions. Because of this, greenhouses were designed so that they could be opened at the ridge or at the side walls for venting air as desired. This is based on natural air movement resulting from the effect of gravity on air (warm air is lighter weight and rises). The hinged ventilators operated by manual machines every 50 feet or so in the greenhouse seemed to be a reasonable method for controlling greenhouse temperatures, but as manpower quality or quantity became more scarce, mechanical control of the ventilators was desired. The electric- or pneumatic-powered systems developed for operation of greenhouse ventilators, if properly installed and operated, can give improved ventilator operation, and they do reduce the need for some manpower. Although some greenhouse operators have developed and installed their own ventilator operating equipment, most growers use existing systems that are on the market, and the installation of these systems was probably handled by the firm from whom they purchased the equipment. Maintenance of ventilator operating machines is quite routine, but maintenance of the ventilators is a continuing problem.

At about the same time the operation of ventilators was being mechanized, fan and pad systems were developed in some parts of the country for cooling greenhouse air during warm weather. These systems used exhaust fans for removing air from the greenhouse, and there was interest in using them on some basis for the exchange of air during cool weather. It was necessary to devise a means of introducing a relatively small quantity of outdoors air uniformly throughout the greenhouse.

For this method, a perforated polyethylene tube is used, with one end of it attached to a shuttered opening in the greenhouse wall, and the other end closed. As the exhaust fans remove air from the greenhouse, air from outdoors fills the tube and is distributed uniformly to the greenhouse through the holes which are punched the length of the tube. This system is designed for cool weather use. It cannot exchange enough air during warm weather to cool the greenhouse adequately.

The air movement required for cool weather ventilation is about 2 cubic feet per minute (cfm) per square foot of greenhouse floor space. This is one-fifth to one-fourth the air movement used for the fan and pad system during warm weather. The location of the fan is not of consequence. The greenhouse crew should be able to put the exhaust fan in place and install the shutter and perforated poly tube, but an electrician should be used for making the electrical connection to the fan. The tube will need to be replaced yearly. The exhaust fan may require lubrication, the belt may need tightening or replacement, and steel parts should be painted as needed.

Instead of using just a perforated poly tube for admittance of air, a tube fan may be added to the system. This is placed between the tube opening and shutter a few inches from the side wall. The direction of air movement from the tube fan is into the tube. The intent is that the tube fan be operated continuously. When the greenhouse temperature is right, the exhaust fan does not operate, the shutter is closed, and the tube fan circulates only greenhouse air. When the greenhouse temperature should be reduced, the exhaust fan is activated, the shutter is opened, and the tube fan circulates a mixture of outdoor and greenhouse air. The greenhouse crew should be able to install the tube fan, but an electrician should make the electricial connection to the fan motor.

- **REDUCING GREENHOUSE TEMPERATURES DURING WARM WEATHER IS HANDLED BY INTRODUCING THE AIR THROUGH A MOIST PAD**

The familiar name for this system is fan and pad—and quite appropriate, because exhaust fans are used to remove air from the greenhouse and the only route left for air to enter the greenhouse is through the moistened pad on the opposite wall. The entering air is cooled in proportion to the rate of water evaporation at the pad. About 8,800 Btu of heat are transferred from the incoming air in the change of one gallon of liquid water to water vapor. During hot weather some of the fans may be operated continuously, but the pads are moistened only during the day. Thus the fan and pad system cools effectively only during the day. If water is supplied to the pads too late in the day or during the night, the greenhouse atmosphere becomes so damp that diseases can be a serious problem.

For average conditions, about 8 cfm of air movement per square foot of floor space should be provided, and about one square foot of pad area is needed for each 150 cfm of air movement. For newly constructed greenhouses, provision should be made to have the pad inside the structure so that it is possible to use the pad or completely close the greenhouse from day to day in the changeable spring and fall weather. If the pad must be constructed outside of the greenhouse, some means of rapid opening or closing of the area should be provided. The maximum water consumption is approximately one gallon per minute per 100 square feet of pad area.

Because of variance in greenhouse structures, crops, sites, and local weather conditions, fan and pad systems must be tailored for the problem at hand. The sellers of the equipment should be able to supply the technical information needed for the proper design of the system. In most instances the greenhouse crew should be able to handle about all of the fan and pad installation except the electrical hook-up.

As an aid in making the decision about installing a fan and pad system, some readings should be made with a sling psychrometer in early afternoon in the greenhouse. The dry bulb reading is the temperature without fan and pad system, and the wet bulb reading will be just a few degrees cooler than the temperature that would be realized with system installed. In general, plant growth is not so good in high temperatures as it is in more moderate ones. What are high temperatures? —85°F. and up.

• REFRIGERATED COOLING INSTALLATION IS A JOB FOR PROFESSIONALS

Working with refrigerated units requires more specialized information and tools than could be expected with the local crew. The best start is to buy reliable equipment from a firm which can give good and prompt service. A routine does need to be established for checking temperatures regularly, cleaning compressor motor and coils, adjusting pulley belt, and checking motor lubrication, but other than that it should be a service call by the refrigeration people.

• THE GREENHOUSE MANAGER MUST ESTABLISH THE GASOLINE ENGINE SERVICING ROUTINE

It is questionable if gasoline engines can be or should be serviced at the greenhouse. Here again the tools and information are lacking. There is no question, however, about the need for regular servicing of this equipment, and the manager must set up a good program. Different methods can be used, but it is difficult to get consistent results unless there is a definite assignment of responsibility for each piece of equipment together with a suitable check list. What needs to be checked, at what interval, and who does the checking? Purely routine or simple maintenance or repair jobs may be handled by those individuals, but for detailed work of any kind the equipment would be taken to the right service or repair shop.

It will help the manager a lot if he realizes at the time he buys gasoline-engine-powered equipment that service and repair will be a big factor. It should be determined at time of purchase if the servicing of the unit can be handled efficiently and promptly.

- **THE GREENHOUSE OPERATOR WHO IS HANDY WITH A WELDER CAN SAVE HIMSELF SOME TIME AND MONEY**

There is a need for both arc and gas welding around the greenhouse—for new construction as well as repair work. The equipment is relatively inexpensive, and the training required is within the reach of most individuals. Work with metal can often be done better and faster by welding than by other means.

- **MACHINES HAVE THE CAPABILITY OF UTILIZATION OF POWER**

There are a lot of different kinds of machines used around the greenhouse. The object in using a machine is to get work done better or faster or to accomplish more work. There is a power input into machines, and hopefully a work output. The primary sources of power are (1) animal, and this is mainly manpower, although through the years it may have been oxen or horse; (2) heat, of which the internal combustion (gasoline) engine is the prime example, although steam may have been used in the past and atomic could possibly be used in the future; and (3) electricity, with which motors of various types and sizes are used.

In the utilization of power the machine may make use of one or more of the six simple machines, which are lever, wheel and axle, pulley, inclined plane, wedge, and screw. As elementary a machine as a shovel is a combination of two simple machines—wedge and lever. Any machine, regardless of how complex, consists of one or more simple machines. There are some very clever combinations and applications of the simple machines, but basically it is the utilization of power with these simple machines that allows more work to be done better and faster.

Reference Reviews

1. Anderson, Edwin P., *Gas Appliances and Heating*, Theodore Audel & Company, Indianapolis, 1967. *Both domestic and commercial units are covered, but there is good basic information on such items as meter reading, gas pipe sizing and installation, some minimum essentials on gas-fired boilers, installing heating lines, gas unit heaters, and the use of accessories like thermostats and gas pressure regulators.*

2. Anonymous, *Commercial Glasshouses—Siting, Types, Construction, and Heating*, Bulletin No. 115, Her Majesty's Stationery Office, London, 1964. *The British approach and methods may differ from some of those in the United States, but the chapters on ventilation and heating systems will be of particular interest.*

3. Anonymous, *Concrete Masonry Handbook*, Portland Cement Association, 33 W. Grand Ave., Chicago, 1951. *A useful reference manual for the construction of walls or buildings from concrete block.*

4. Anonymous, *Design and Control of Concrete Mixtures*, Tenth Edition, Portland Cement Association, 33 W. Grand Ave., Chicago, 1952. *A complete coverage of concrete and its uses, from fundamental facts to special types of concrete.*

5. Anonymous, *Electric Gardening*, Second Edition, Edison Electric Institute, 750 Third Ave., New York, 1970. *A rather broad and general discussion of the use or possible uses of electricity in greenhouses. It is written for the hobbyist as well as the commercial grower.*

6. Anonymous, *Electric Growing*, The Electricity Council, Trafalgar Buildings, 1 Charing Cross, London S.W. 1, 1971. *All possible uses of electricity in the greenhouse are discussed. Probably of most interest to growers who want to compare applications in Great Britain and the United States.*

7. Anonymous, *Electric Motors for Farm Use*, Vocational Agriculture Service, University of Illinois, Urbana, 1967. *A basic guide on the selection, installation, and care of electric motors.*

8. Anonymous, *Farmstead Wiring Handbook*, Third Edition, Edison Electric Institute, 750 Third Ave., New York, 1965. *Although this manual was written specifically for planning the farm wiring system, most of the information is directly applicable to electric service around the greenhouse.*

9. Anonymous, *Myers Electric Motor Technical Manual*, The F. E. Myers & Bro. Co., 400 Orange St., Ashland, Ohio 44805, 1962. *A very thorough*

coverage from what electricity is to what electric motors are, different types of motors, variations in motor construction, and wiring needs. It contains a glossary of electrical terms.

10. Baker, Kenneth F., et al., *The U.C. System for Producing Healthy Container-Grown Plants*, Manual 23, California Agricultural Experiment Station Extension Service, Berkeley, 1957. *Chapters 8 through 10 give information and recommendations on steaming soil—volume of steam required, soil preparation, costs of steaming, and the equipment used in steaming soil.*

11. Boyd, L. L., *Know Your Concrete*, Bulletin 847, Cornell University, Ithaca, New York, 1954. *It is well illustrated and discusses material, proportioning, tools and equipment, mixing, placing, forms, finishing, and curing.*

12. Canham, A. E., *Artificial Light in Horticulture*, Centrex Publishing Company, Eindhoven, The Netherlands, 1966. *Chapter 1, "Light and Its Measurement," and Chapter 3, "Lamps," have useful information on these subjects not easily located in other sources.*

13. Field, Edwin M., *Oil Burners*, Second Edition, Theodore Audel & Company, Indianapolis, 1970. *The title does not do it justice. Actually it covers everything associated with the use of oil burners—petroleum, the definition of heat, heating systems, combustion, oil burner components such as nozzle, pumps, and blowers, ignition systems, electrical wiring and controls, oil storage and trouble shooting.*

14. Gray, Harold E., *Greenhouse Heating and Construction*, Florists' Publishing Co., Chicago, 1956. *It is particularly helpful in figuring heat load, pipe sizing, and arrangement of heating lines.*

15. Jones, Mack M., *Shopwork on the Farm*, Second Edition, McGraw-Hill Book Company, New York, 1955. *It is clearly written and liberally illustrated and would be a good book to introduce the greenhouse worker to such engineering tasks as the managing of the shop and tools, minor construction, concrete work, pipe handling, and welding.*

16. Merritt, Frederick S., et al., *Building Construction Handbook*, Second Edition, McGraw-Hill Book Company, New York, 1965. *Although this book was written for the non-specialist, it contains very detailed information about all aspects of construction. It is not for the beginner, but the manager who will be involved in various kinds of construction work will find it invaluable.*

17. Oravetz, Jules, Sr., *Plumbers and Pipe Fitters Library—Drainage, Fittings, Fixtures*, Theodore Audel & Company, Indianapolis, 1968. *Portions of this book refer specifically to the plumbing trade, but Chapter 1, "Water Supply" Chapter 5, "Pipe Fittings," and Chapter 7, "Valves and Faucets," contain information that can be put to use around the greenhouse.*

18. ————————————, *Plumbers and Pipe Fitters Library—*

Installation, Heating, Welding, Theodore Audel & Company, Indianapolis, 1968. *The most applicable chapters in this book are Chapter 1, "Pipe Fitting," and Chapter 9, "Brazing and Welding." Because so much pipe fitting is done in the greenhouse, Chapter 1 is very worthwhile.*

19. _____, *Plumbers and Pipe Fitters Library— Materials, Tools, Calculations*, Theodore Audel & Company, Indianapolis, 1968. *There is a wealth of information in this book for the greenhouse engineer. Chapter 1, "Mathematics," and Chapter 2, "Physics for Plumbers and Pipe Fitters," are loaded with a practical presentation of basic facts and concepts that are essential for many kinds of engineering. Chapter 5, "Pipe", Chapter 6, "Tools," Chapter 7, "Soldering," and Chapter 10, "General Plumbing Information," take up some of the specifics of the trade which apply to greenhouse work.*

20. Palmer, M. L., et al., *Private Water Systems, Midwest Plan Service—14*, Cooperative Extension Service, Ohio State University, Columbus, 1968. *This manual will be of interest to greenhouse operators who have to develop their own water sources.*

21. Parker, Marvin M., *Farm Welding*, Third Edition, McGraw-Hill Book Company, New York, 1958. *The basic principles and instructions for arc welding and oxyacetylene welding and cutting are given and illustrated.*

22. Phipps, Lloyd J., *Mechanics in Agriculture*, The Interstate Printers & Publishers, Inc., Danville, Illinois, 1967. *A good book for the beginner, covering all aspects of mechanical work. It is well illustrated and contains the necessary data tables.*

23. Richey, C. B., Paul Jacobson, and Carl W. Hall, *Agricultural Engineers Handbook*, McGraw-Hill Book Company, New York, 1961. *Much of the subject matter here refers specifically to farming operations, but of course some of these relate to greenhouse work also. This would be a book for the manager who wants more detailed information on some certain subjects. Chapters of interest probably would be Chapter 3, "Power-Transmission Elements," Chapter 9, "Fuels and Combustion," Chapter 35, "Land Leveling and Grading," Chapter 36, "Agricultural Drainage," Chapter 46, "Structural Requirements for Farm Buildings," and Chapter 51, "Electrical Equipment."*

24. Roberts, W. J., *Heating and Ventilating Greenhouses*, Cooperative Extension Service, Rutgers University, New Brunswick, New Jersey, 1969. *The information presented here is primarily for the smaller, plastic film greenhouses.*

25. Teter, Norman C., *Foundations for Farm Buildings*, Farmers' Bulletin No. 1869, U.S. Department of Agriculture, Washington, 1965. *Fundamental foundation facts are supplied which are needed for buildings that might be erected in conjunction with the greenhouse operation.*

26. _____, *Use of Concrete on the Farm*, Farmers'

Bulletin No. 2203, U.S. Department of Agriculture, Washington, 1965. *Instructions on handling concrete, and typical uses of it on the farm.*
27. Wakeman, T. J., and Vernon Lee McCoy, *The Farm Shop*, The Macmillan Company, New York, 1960. *A book for the beginner on the various types of mechanical work.*

CHAPTER 4

Crop Rotations and Scheduling

CHAPTER 4

The objective of rotations and scheduling is to provide the maximum flower or plant production in the greenhouse space available for the best net dollar return.

Depending on the crops to be produced, the rotation and schedule may be combined or separate. In the rotation it is determined whether the crops will fit in the area available for the time period in question. This is an over-all and usually a long-term view of the utilization of space. The schedule gives the pertinent details, step by step, that are necessary for producing the crops in the allotted time. Both must be a matter of written record. The form of the rotation or schedule will vary with the crop. Each manager must devise the method for delineating the rotation and schedule that fits the situation at hand. It is best to start with ruled sheets 8½″ ×11″ and then make the vertical columns that are needed. Paper ruled the 8½-inch width will be suitable for most of this work. In instances where a greater number of columns are required, paper ruled the 11-inch dimension should be obtained.

The first step is to assess the potential market in relation to the production capabilities of your greenhouse area. If a market need can be established at good return, then the rotation must be developed to provide the crops at those times. These may be simple one-crop rotations, or extremely complex ones in which timing and execution of production plans are critical. It is difficult to use an area economically and efficiently with a mixed rotation of cut flowers and pot plants. If both cut flowers and pot plants are produced at one place of business, each type of crop should rotate in its own area. The needs for the two types of crops are sufficiently different so that it takes time and expense to convert an area from one type of crop to the other.

The rotation needs to project planting and cropping plans for the next several months or several years; and happily, if estimates and plans have been good, the rotation may be used without making changes in mid-course. If changes must be made, the effects on the long-range plans must be evaluated before putting them in operation.

The production area needs to be simply and clearly indentified. Numerical identification is usually best—a system such as numbering the houses from north to south and the benches within each house from north to south. Thus a given bench may be identified as 2-3, and that immediately establishes it as the third bench in the second house. In larger houses that are divided by a central walk, it may be helpful to use east and west designations for each half-house; and then the bench identified as 1-2W would be the second bench in the west half of house 1. A sketch of the greenhouse area, with identification numbers, should be posted where workers or visitors may refer to it.

The exact dimensions of each bench must be a matter of record that can be referred to easily, and whenever posible the record should also indicate the spacing for various kinds of plants on the bench and the total number of plants it holds.

The possibilities for variations in rotations are almost infinite. The examples which are used here are just a few of the ways they may be developed. The purpose here is to illustrate methods and techniques rather than to provide rotations that one may lift in entirety and use in his situation. The steps that are used in developing these examples and the records that are used should fit most commercial situations, but the details must necessarily differ from place to place.

Cut Flower Rotations

• ROSE ROTATION AND CROPPING

Potential market: The flowers would be marketed through three wholesale commission houses within good shipping or delivery distance, and the survey indicates a need for about one million hybrid tea roses per year, with reduced production in the summer and generally good demand September through May. The extra demand for holidays would be about 5,000 for Sweetest Day; 10,000 for Christmas;

20,000 for Valentine's Day; 20,000 for Easter; and 40,000 for Mother's Day. The color distribution is 80 per cent red, 10 per cent yellow, 5 per cent pink, and 5 per cent white. The need for sweetheart roses is about 200,000, and the color distribution is 50 per cent pink, 25 per cent red, 10 per cent yellow, 10 per cent white, and 5 per cent other colors.

Greenhouse area: There are six separate houses (Fig. 4-1), each 42 feet × 212 feet, with a central walk. Each house has 16 benches 3½ feet × 100 feet, making a total of 96 benches for the range. The plants would be spaced four across the bench and 100 rows per bench—a total of 400 plants per bench. Eighty-four benches would be planted to hybrid teas—a total of 33,600 plants, and twelve benches would have sweetheart rose plants—4,800 plants.

It is planned to replant one-fourth of the range each four years—21 benches of hybrid teas (8,400 plants) and 3 benches of sweethearts (1,200 plants). Approximately one-third of the replanting would be done in January and cropped for Easter; one-third replanted in February and cropped for Mother's Day; and the remaining one-third would be replanted in late May and early June. Cut-back of second year and older plants would be started in late May and completed in August.

It usually is easier to do the work of planting and cropping by the house or half-house rather than by the bench. In this rose range it is planned to operate it with three growers, each in charge of adjacent houses. One of the purposes of the rotation and cropping plan is to distribute the work of planting, cut-back, and pinching equally over the range. The plan used here provides for the planting of one half-house per year in each grower's area. That sets the stage for distributing the work load.

Reduced flower production would result during the summer because of the replanting in May and the cut-back of the older plants during the summer.

Increased flower production for the holiday markets would be controlled by pinching at the calculated time in advance of the holiday. In addition, the flower production for Easter and Mother's Day would be increased by the replanting done in January and February. It is planned to establish a cropping cycle with plants that are going to

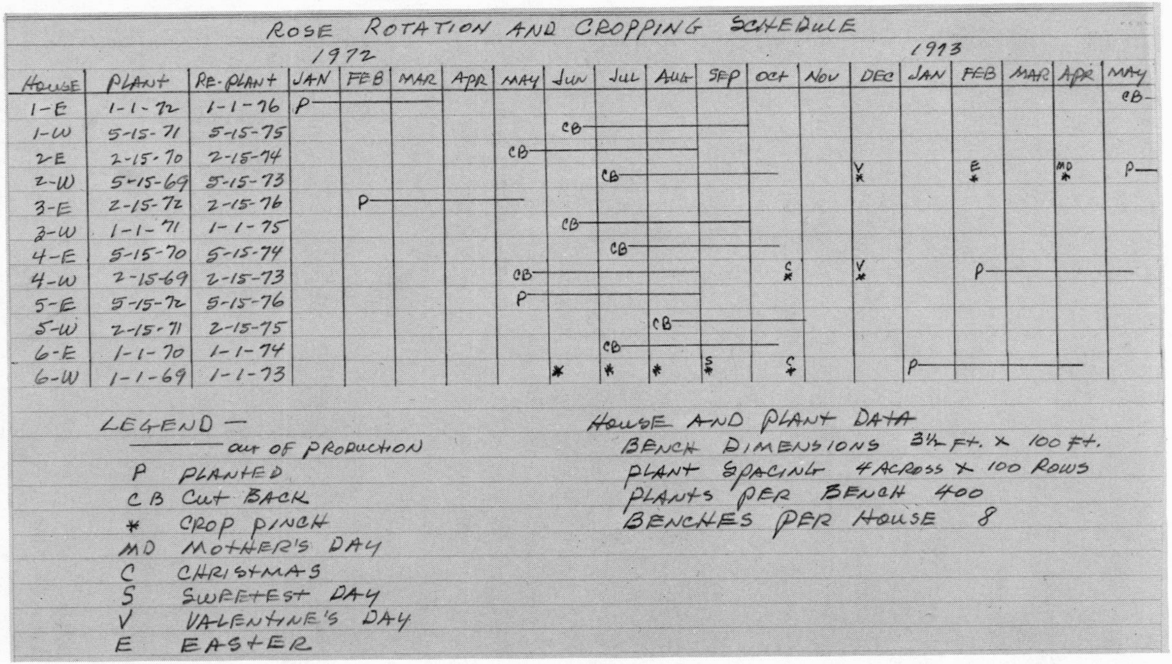

ROSE ROTATION AND CROPPING SCHEDULE

HOUSE	PLANT	RE-PLANT	1972 JAN	FEB	MAR	APR	MAY	JUN	JUL	AUG	SEP	OCT	NOV	DEC	1973 JAN	FEB	MAR	APR	MAY
1-E	1-1-72	1-1-76	P																CB
1-W	5-15-71	5-15-75						CB											
2-E	2-15-70	2-15-74					CB												
2-W	5-15-69	5-15-73							CB					V *		E *		MD *	P
3-E	2-15-72	2-15-76		P															
3-W	1-1-71	1-1-75						CB											
4-E	5-15-70	5-15-74							CB										
4-W	2-15-69	2-15-73					CB					C *		V *		P			
5-E	5-15-72	5-15-76					P												
5-W	2-15-71	2-15-75								CB									
6-E	1-1-70	1-1-74							CB										
6-W	1-1-69	1-1-73						*	*	*	S *	C *			P				

LEGEND —
——— out of production
P PLANTED
CB Cut BACK
* CROP PINCH
MD MOTHER'S DAY
C CHRISTMAS
S SWEETEST DAY
V VALENTINE'S DAY
E EASTER

HOUSE AND PLANT DATA
BENCH DIMENSIONS 3½ Ft. X 100 Ft.
PLANT SPACING 4 ACROSS X 100 ROWS
PLANTS PER BENCH 400
BENCHES PER HOUSE 8

Fig. 4—1. A reproduction of the rose foreman's rotation and cropping schedule. The rotation provides for flower production during the best market periods and even distribution of the work load of planting and cut-back.

be removed for replanting of a house. The plants, which are going to be removed in late December to clear the house for planting in early January, would not be cut back during the summer. A pinching program would be started on these plants in late May and continued through the summer to cycle cropping for Sweetest Day and Christmas. The plants to be removed mid-February would be cut back June 1 and pinched to crop for Sweetest Day, Christmas, and Valentine's Day. The plants to be removed in mid-May would be pinched the first two weeks of December and should cycle for Valentine's Day and Mother's Day. With Easter in early April, these plants also would crop for Easter.

The immediate objective with a newly planted started eye rose plant is to develop good canes from the base of the plant. This can be done best by selective pinching until the plant structure is established, and then proceed with flower production. However, with the plants benched in early spring it is reasonable to plan to cut two flowers per plant for the holiday and then to continue pinching during the summer to build the plant as needed. The plants should be benched about 12 weeks before the expected crop for the holiday. Flowers would be allowed to develop on the stronger canes if the timing was about right for the holiday, or they would be pinched 7 to 8 weeks before desired time to cut. Weaker shoots should be pinched as soon as three or four 5-leaflet leaves have cleared. Two flowers per plant for the holiday cut could be expected from such a program—in this instance, 16,800 hybrid tea flowers. The additional 4,000 to 24,000 required for Easter and Mother's Day would have to come from other plants in the range, from stems that were either cut or pinched approximately seven weeks before the holiday.

Plants benched in late spring should be pinched and grown up until a good plant structure is developed. This usually will require double or triple pinching and 12 to 15 weeks before flower production will start on the new plants.

Cut-back of the older plants should be started after Mother's Day and then so scheduled that the work of doing it as well as the subsequent pinching of the plants will be spaced sufficiently so that it can be handled. This also will distribute flower production more evenly.

Cut-back plants will need to be pinched, and some stems double pinched. This keeps them out of production for 9 to 12 weeks.

Control of cropping of roses is not too involved. If it is desired to cut 10,000 roses for Christmas, the number of flowers cut eight weeks before Christmas is subtracted from the total crop to determine how many pinches to make. At that time of the year it is known that a flowering stem will not result from each stem that is cut or pinched, so a greater number of stems will be pinched—possibly 25 per cent more. About the same timing and procedure are needed for the Valentine's Day cut. Unfortunately this means that the return crop from the Christmas cut is just a bit late for Valentine's Day. Easters in early April make the timing just about right for the return crop from the Valentine's Day cut, and incidentally this also makes the timing about right for the return crop from the Easter cut to hit the Mother's Day market.

It usually is considered that six to eight weeks are required, depending on the time of the year, from the time a rose stem is pinched or cut until the resulting flower can be cut. However, there are several variables that keep the game of rose cropping interesting. It certainly is true that the time of the year does have an effect on the length of time to produce a rose flower. The timing in late spring to early fall may be five to six weeks, and from late fall to early winter about eight weeks, but natural environmental conditions vary sufficiently from year to year to affect the timing by several days for exactly the same period of the year. The other notable effect on timing is the temperature maintained in the greenhouses—less time is required with higher temperatures. In fact temperatures can be used to adjust the time for flowering; and because of this it is helpful to have the plants cropped in houses separate from the others, rather than scattered through the range, so that the temperature may be adjusted as needed. The crop is a few days earlier from stems hard pinched than from cut stems. Flower development from stems soft pinched requires about one week longer.

In the first year, the rule-of-thumb recommendations for timing should be used, but it is important that detailed records be kept of just what was done and what the results were. Included in this record should be an assessment of the general weather conditions during the cropping period. Crop timing will be different in various geographic locations. The only timing recommendations which will be consistent are those developed by each grower at his own place.

• CARNATION ROTATION AND CROPPING

A survey of local market conditions indicates that although most of the demand is met by carnations flown in from California and Colorado, there still is a need for premium flowers produced locally. One wholesale commission house would be used, and it could handle about 500,000 flowers per year. The color distribution should be approximately 45 per cent light pink; 30 per cent white; 15 per cent red; and 10 per cent other colors. There is less demand for carnations late June through August, and the market is particularly strong for red flowers for Christmas and Valentine's Day. There is a steady but small demand for miniatures.

The carnation range would consist of six houses 36½ feet × 110 feet (Fig. 4-2). Each house would have seven benches, each 3½ feet × 100 feet. The plants would be benched eight across the bench and 150 rows—1,200 plants per bench. There would be 18 benches light pink, 12 benches white, 6 red, 4 other colors, and 2 miniatures. The new plants would be benched in February, May, and June. The three benches of red carnations cropped for Christmas and Valentine's Day would be replaced with two benches of light pink and one bench of white in February. These plants would provide some flower production during the summer. In mid-May approximately one-half of the range would be replanted—eight benches light pink, five white, three red, two other colors, and one miniature. The remaining benches would be replanted in mid-June—eight benches light pink, six white, three red, two other colors, and one miniature.

The time of flower production will be controlled to an extent by pinching. In the February planting the plants would be pinched in mid-March. In late April or May the stems forming flower buds would be pinched. Flower production from these benches would then start in June and continue through the summer and on. The plants benched in mid-May would be pinched in June and then the pinching con-

CARNATION ROTATION IN 42-BENCH AREA

BENCH NUMBERS	PLANT DATE	FLOWER COLOR	FLOWERING PERIOD	RE-PLANT DATE	FLOWER COLOR	FLOWERING PERIOD	RE-PLANT DATE	FLOWER COLOR	FLOWERING PERIOD
1	2-15-72	WHITE	JUN-MAY	5-15-73	RED	SEP-FEB	2-15-74	WHITE	JUN-MAY
2-3	2-15-72	PINK	JUN-MAY	6-15-73	RED	SEP-FEB	2-15-74	PINK	JUN-MAY
4	5-15-72	RED	SEP-FEB	2-15-73	WHITE	JUN-MAY	5-15-74	RED	SEP-FEB
5-6	5-15-72	RED	SEP-FEB	2-15-73	PINK	JUN-MAY	5-15-74	RED	SEP-FEB
7-14	5-15-72	PINK	SEP-MAY	5-15-73	PINK	SEP-MAY	5-15-74	PINK	SEP-MAY
15-19	5-15-72	WHITE	SEP-MAY	5-15-73	WHITE	SEP-MAY	5-15-74	WHITE	SEP-MAY
20-21	5-15-72	OTHER	SEP-MAY	5-15-73	OTHER	SEP-MAY	5-15-74	OTHER	SEP-MAY
22	5-15-72	MINI	SEP-MAY	5-15-73	MINI	SEP-MAY	5-15-74	MINI	SEP-MAY
23-30	6-15-72	PINK	OCT-JUN	6-15-73	PINK	OCT-JUN	6-15-74	PINK	OCT-JUN
31-36	6-15-72	WHITE	OCT-JUN	6-15-73	WHITE	OCT-JUN	6-15-74	WHITE	OCT-JUN
37-39	6-15-72	RED	OCT-JUN	6-15-73	RED	OCT-JUN	6-15-74	RED	OCT-JUN
40-41	6-15-72	OTHER	OCT-JUN	6-15-73	OTHER	OCT-JUN	6-15-74	OTHER	OCT-JUN
42	6-15-72	MINI	OCT-JUN	6-15-73	MINI	OCT-JUN	6-15-74	MINI	OCT-JUN

Fig. 4—2. A reproduction of the carnation foreman's rotation sheet. By rotating the two sets of three benches (1-3 and 4-6), additional red carnations can be cropped for Valentine's Day, and some pink and white flowers are produced for the summer market.

tinued until September on stems forming flower buds. This would provide flower production from early fall and on. It is important to do whatever pinching can be done daily in the period from August 15 to September 15 because a variation in a day or two of pinching at that time of the year might space the flower production a few weeks during the winter. The plants benched in June would be pinched in mid-July, and pinching would be continued until September on stems forming flower buds.

The red plants benched in May would be scheduled for cropping for Valentine's Day by pinching as many stems as possible around mid-August. These plants would then be removed after that crop. From the red plants planted in June it would be planned to get the Christmas crop plus production for the remainder of the season. Pinches made in late July and early August should be right for the Christmas crop.

The plants that are to be removed in May would be lighted in January in order to increase the flower production in May before their removal. The plants that are to be removed in June would be lighted in February to increase flower production from them in late May and June.

• CHRYSANTHEMUM ROTATION AND CROPPING

This would be a standard mum program to supply the flowers needed for the wholesale commission house owned and operated by the firm that also produces other cut flowers and pot plants. The year-round requirements for standard mums is 200 dozen per week. The market demand is for about the same quantity each week, but the color distribution varies with the season—September-December, 40 per cent yellow, 25 per cent white, 25 per cent bronze, and 10 per cent pink; December, 30 per cent yellow, 45 per cent white, 15 per cent bronze, and 10 per cent pink; January-May, 40 per cent yellow, 45 per cent white; 5 per cent bronze, and 10 per cent pink; May-September, 40 per cent yellow, 50 per cent white, and 10 per cent pink. Indianapolis varieties would be used from October to December, Mefos from December to April, Nob Hills from April to July, and Southern Comfort and Southern Gold from July through September.

STANDARD MUM ROTATION — SINGLE-STEM   MARCH 1972

UNIT	PLANT	FLOWER	PLANT	FLOWER	PLANT	FLOWER	PLANT	FLOWER
1	SEP 11	JAN 1	JAN 8	APR 9	APR 16	JUL 2	JUL 9	OCT 1
2	18	8	15	16	23	9	16	8
3	25	15	22	23	30	16	23	15
4	OCT 2	22	29	30	MAY 7	23	30	22
5	9	29	FEB 5	MAY 7	14	30	AUG 6	29
6	16	FEB 5	12	14	21	AUG 6	13	NOV 12
7	23	12	19	21	28	13	20	19
8	30	19	26	28	JUN 4	20	27	26
9	NOV 6	26	MAR 5	28	4	20	27	DEC 3
10	20	MAR 5	12	JUN 4	11	27	SEP 3	17
11	27	12	19	11	18	SEP 3	10	24
12	DEC 4	19	26	18	25	10	17	31
13	11	26	APR 2	25	JUL 2	17	24	JAN 7
14	18	APR 2	9	25	2	17	24	14
15	JAN 1	9	16	JUL 2	9	24	OCT 1	21

EACH BENCH 3½ FT. X 100 FT.   PLANT 8 ACROSS X 300 ROWS - 2,400 CUTTINGS

VARIETIES — DEC-APR   MEFOS
           APR- JUL   NOB HILLS
           JUL - SEP   SOUTHERNS
           OCT - DEC   INDIANAPOLIS

COLOR DISTRIBUTION   WHT.   YEL.   BR.   PINK
         SEP - DEC   25%   40%   25%   10%
         DEC   45%   30%   15%   10%
         JAN - MAY   45%   40%   5%   10%
         MAY - SEP   50%   40%   —   10%

Fig. 4—3. A reproduction of the chrysanthemum foreman's rotation sheet. Planting dates were determined from the scheduling table (Fig. 4—6) by using the variety classification from Fig. 4—4.

This mum program would be in houses with benches 3½ feet × 100 feet (Fig. 4-3). The plants would be grown single stem (not pinched) and spaced eight plants across the bench and 4 inches between rows, with 300 rows to the bench (2,400 cuttings per bench). Fifteen benches would be used in this rotation. The houses would be equipped with carbon dioxide generators which would provide 1,000 ppm CO_2 during the daytime, from November through April.

For years chrysanthemums have been classified according to the number of weeks required from the start of short days to the time of flowering, and this has been called response. The response classification was based on the performance of the particular variety when grown in natural season during the fall, and it is an adequate classification system for plants grown that time of the year. However, plants of the same response group grown other times of the year may perform variably. A 10-week variety may actually respond in 9 weeks in the spring or in 11 weeks during the summer, while others maintain the same rate of response the year-round. Then, too, varieties within the same response group do not all grow at the same rate; given the same growing environment, some always grow taller than others. Proper rotation and scheduling is difficult if the classification system does not provide a workable delineation of the individuals. A double-number timing classification system should be used which definitely specifies the total number of weeks for the crop and the number of weeks of short days the variety should have for the time of the year it will be flowered. Such a system (Fig. 4-4 and 4-5) was developed for presentation here. With this numerical system the first number is the total number of weeks from planting to flowering and the second number is the number of weeks from start of short days to flowering. Because of variable growing conditions from one season of the year to another, the classification numbers for the variety must change accordingly. This system was developed for the average climatic conditions at Columbus, Ohio; and for areas in which the climate varies from Columbus conditions, the classifications would need to be changed accordingly.

The scheduling table (Fig. 4-6) is a universal table designed for use with the double-number classification system. It indicates the planting date and the start-of-short-days date for any variety to be flowered at a given time, if the proper timing classification is used for that variety.

If varieties with the same timing classification are used in a planting, it could be expected that they would flower at about the same height and at the same time. When Trident and Promenade (timing classification 12-9) are flowered during the summer with the Nob Hills and handled on the Nob Hill timing classification (12-10), they would flower about one week earlier on shorter stems. Deep Champagne grown with May Shoesmith and Imp. Rivalry on their timing classification would flower at the same time but would be taller.

The timing classification used here is for single-stem crops. For

Standard Chrysanthemum Single-Stem Timing Classification

Classification for Month of Flowering

Variety	Jan	Feb	Mar	Apr	May	Jun	Jul	Aug	Sep	Oct	Nov	Dec
Southern Comfort	—	—	—	—	—	11-9	11-9	11-9	11-9	—	—	—
Gt. Betsy Ross	—	—	—	—	—	—	11-9	11-9	11-9	12-9	—	—
Southern Gold	—	—	—	—	—	11-9	11-9	11-9	11-9	—	—	—
Imp. Detroit News	—	—	—	—	—	—	—	—	11-9	12-9	—	—
Promenade	15-9	15-9	14-9	13-9	12-9	11-9	11-9	11-9	11-9	12-9	13-9	14-9
#4 Imp. Ind. Wht.	15-9	15-9	14-9	13-9	—	—	—	—	—	12-9	13-9	14-9
#4 Imp. Ind. Yel.	15-9	15-9	14-9	13-9	—	—	—	—	—	12-9	13-9	14-9
CF 2 Ind. Br.	15-9	15-9	14-9	13-9	—	—	—	—	—	12-9	13-9	14-9
#2 Ind. Dk. Br.	15-9	15-9	14-9	13-9	—	—	—	—	—	12-9	13-9	14-9
#4 Imp. Ind. Pk.	15-9	15-9	14-9	13-9	—	—	—	—	—	12-9	13-9	14-9
Super Chief	—	—	—	—	13-9	12-9	12-9	12-9	12-9	13-9	—	—
Don. Wht. Spider	—	—	—	14-9	13-9	12-9	12-9	12-9	12-9	13-9	—	—
CF Good News	—	—	—	—	—	12-9	12-9	12-9	12-9	13-9	—	—
Luyona	—	—	—	14-9	13-9	12-9	12-9	12-9	12-9	13-9	—	—
Detroit News	—	—	—	—	—	—	—	12-9	12-9	13-9	—	—
Trident	—	—	—	—	13-9	12-9	12-9	12-9	12-9	13-9	—	—
Promenade	16-9	16-9	15-9	14-9	13-9	12-9	12-9	12-9	12-9	13-9	14-9	15-9
Imp. Ind. Wht.	16-9	16-9	15-9	14-9	—	—	—	—	—	13-9	14-9	15-9
Imp. Ind. Yel.	16-9	16-9	15-9	14-9	—	—	—	—	—	13-9	14-9	15-9
Ind. Br.	16-9	16-9	15-9	14-9	—	—	—	—	—	13-9	14-9	15-9
Dk. Ind. Br.	16-9	16-9	15-9	14-9	—	—	—	—	—	13-9	14-9	15-9
Ind. Pk.	16-9	16-9	15-9	14-9	—	—	—	—	—	13-9	14-9	15-9
Imp. Fred Shoesmith	15-10	15-10	14-10	13-10	—	—	—	—	—	12-10	13-10	14-10
#2 Gold. Shoesmith	15-10	15-10	14-10	13-10	—	—	—	—	—	12-10	13-10	14-10
Nob Hill	—	—	—	—	13-10	12-10	12-10	12-10	12-10	13-10	—	—
Yel. Nob Hill	—	—	—	—	13-10	12-10	12-10	12-10	12-10	13-10	—	—
Fred Shoesmith	16-10	16-10	15-10	14-10	—	—	—	—	—	13-10	14-10	15-10
Imp. Mefo	16-10	16-10	15-10	14-10	—	—	—	—	—	13-10	14-10	15-10
Fuji Mefo	16-10	16-10	15-10	14-10	—	—	—	—	—	13-10	14-10	15-10
Imp. Yel. Mefo	16-10	16-10	15-10	14-10	—	—	—	—	—	13-10	14-10	15-10
Yel. Knight	16-10	16-10	15-10	14-10	13-10	12-10	12-10	12-10	12-10	13-10	14-10	15-10
Mrs. Roy	—	—	—	14-10	13-10	12-10	12-10	12-10	12-10	13-10	14-10	15-10
Br. Streamer	16-10	16-10	15-10	14-10	—	—	—	—	—	—	14-10	15-10
Streamer	16-10	16-10	15-10	14-10	13-10	12-10	12-10	12-10	12-10	13-10	14-10	15-10
Brt. Rosamund	16-10	16-10	15-10	14-10	13-10	12-10	12-10	12-10	12-10	13-10	14-10	15-10
Centennial Mefo	16-11	16-11	15-11	14-11	13-11	—	—	—	—	13-11	14-11	15-11
Goldburst Mefo	16-11	16-11	15-11	14-11	13-11	—	—	—	—	—	14-11	15-11
Tan Vedova	16-11	16-11	15-11	14-11	—	—	—	—	—	13-11	14-11	15-11
Br. Venoya	16-11	16-11	15-11	14-11	—	—	—	—	—	13-11	14-11	15-11
Imp. Pk. Mefo	16-11	16-11	15-11	14-11	—	—	—	—	—	—	14-11	15-11
Deep Champagne	16-11	16-11	15-11	14-11	—	—	—	—	—	—	14-11	15-11
May Shoesmith	17-11	17-11	16-11	15-11	14-11	—	—	—	—	—	15-11	16-11
Imp. Rivalry	17-11	17-11	16-11	15-11	14-11	—	—	—	—	—	15-11	16-11

Fig. 4—4

growing pinched crops, two weeks' time would need to be added to the total crop time. The timing classification for #4 Imp. Ind. White flowered single-stem in November is 13-9; however, if it was to be grown as a pinched crop the timing classification would be 15-9, and the pinch would be made about two weeks after planting. A single-stem standard program is used in this example. Later a pinched

Spray Chrysanthemum Single–Stem Timing Classification

Classification for Month of Flowering

Variety	Jan	Feb	Mar	Apr	May	Jun	Jul	Aug	Sep	Oct	Nov	Dec
Polaris	—	—	14–9	13–9	12–9	11–9	11–9	11–9	11–9	12–9	13–9	—
Arctic	—	—	—	13–9	12–9	11–9	11–9	11–9	11–9	12–9	—	—
#2 Whitechip	—	—	—	—	—	11–9	11–9	11–9	11–9	—	—	—
Nimrod	—	—	—	13–9	12–9	11–9	11–9	11–9	11–9	12–9	—	—
White Marble	—	—	—	13–9	12–9	11–9	11–9	11–9	11–9	12–9	—	—
Yellow Polaris	—	—	14–9	13–9	12–9	11–9	11–9	11–9	11–9	12–9	13–9	—
#2 Yellow Chip	—	—	—	—	—	11–9	11–9	11–9	11–9	—	—	—
Yellow Showoff	—	—	—	—	12–9	11–9	11–9	11–9	11–9	12–9	—	—
Cavalier	—	—	—	13–9	12–9	11–9	11–9	11–9	11–9	12–9	—	—
Florida Marble	—	—	—	13–9	12–9	11–9	11–9	11–9	11–9	12–9	—	—
Flame Belair	—	—	—	13–9	12–9	11–9	11–9	11–9	11–9	12–9	—	—
Red Showoff	—	—	—	13–9	12–9	11–9	11–9	11–9	11–9	12–9	—	—
Copperchip	—	—	—	—	12–9	11–9	11–9	11–9	11–9	12–9	—	—
Dazzler	—	—	—	13–9	12–9	11–9	11–9	11–9	11–9	12–9	—	—
Gay Marble	—	—	—	13–9	12–9	11–9	11–9	11–9	11–9	12–9	—	—
Belair	—	—	—	13–9	12–9	11–9	11–9	11–9	11–9	12–9	13–9	—
Dolly	—	—	—	—	12–9	11–9	11–9	11–9	11–9	12–9	—	—
Imp. Bluechip	—	—	—	—	12–9	11–9	11–9	11–9	11–9	12–9	—	—
Coral Marble	—	—	—	13–9	12–9	11–9	11–9	11–9	11–9	12–9	—	—
Manatee Iceberg	—	—	—	14–10	13–10	12–10	12–10	12–10	12–10	13–10	—	—
Dawn Star	—	—	—	14–10	13–10	12–10	12–10	12–10	12–10	13–10	—	—
#2 Shasta	—	—	—	14–10	13–10	12–10	12–10	12–10	12–10	13–10	—	—
Dk. Yel. Iceberg	—	—	—	14–10	13–10	12–10	12–10	12–10	12–10	13–10	—	—
Yel. Dawn Star	—	—	—	14–10	13–10	12–10	12–10	12–10	12–10	13–10	—	—
Yel. Beauregard	—	—	—	—	13–10	12–10	12–10	12–10	12–10	13–10	—	—
#2 Yel. Shasta	—	—	—	14–10	13–10	12–10	12–10	12–10	12–10	13–10	—	—
Dillon Beauregard	—	—	—	—	13–10	12–10	12–10	12–10	12–10	13–10	—	—
Red Jetfire	—	—	—	—	13–10	12–10	12–10	12–10	12–10	13–10	—	—
#2 Pennant	—	—	—	14–10	13–10	12–10	12–10	12–10	12–10	13–10	—	—
Bright 'N Cheerful	—	—	—	14–10	13–10	12–10	12–10	12–10	12–10	13–10	—	—
Iceland	15–11	15–11	14–11	—	—	—	—	—	—	—	13–11	14–11
Northern Lights	15–11	15–11	14–11	—	—	—	—	—	—	—	13–11	14–11
Jubilee	15–11	15–11	14–11	—	—	—	—	—	—	—	13–11	14–11
Caravelle	15–11	15–11	14–11	—	—	—	—	—	—	—	13–11	14–11
Divinity	16–11	16–11	15–11	14–11 ~	—	—	—	—	—	—	14–11	15–11
Yel. Divinity	16–11	16–11	15–11	14–11	—	—	—	—	—	—	14–11	15–11
Br. Venoya	16–11	16–11	15–11	—	—	—	—	—	—	13–11	14–11	15–11
Demure	16–11	16–11	15–11	—	—	—	—	—	—	13–11	14–11	15–11

Fig. 4—5

standard and spray program will be used as an example in a retail greenhouse.

In developing a cut chrysanthemum program, it is necessary to determine what kind of a cropping schedule can be maintained in the allotted area. A rotation chart should be made first which gives the planting dates and flowering dates in each bench for a period of about two years. Usually with a cut flower rotation it is desired to have as uniform flower production throughout the year as possible. The rotation chart shows how the space is being utilized and gives

Chrysanthemum Cut Flower Scheduling Table

Flowering Date	Planting Dates								Start-of-Short-Day Dates		
	19	18	17	16	15	14	13	12	11	10	9
Jan 1	8/21	8/28	9/ 4	9/11	9/18	—	—	—	10/16	10/23	10/30
Jan 8	8/28	9/ 4	9/11	9/18	9/25	—	—	—	10/23	10/30	11/ 6
Jan 15	9/ 4	9/11	9/18	9/25	10/ 2	—	—	—	10/30	11/ 6	11/13
Jan 22	9/11	9/18	9/25	10/ 2	10/ 9	—	—	—	11/ 6	11/13	11/20
Jan 29	9/18	9/25	10/ 2	10/ 9	10/16	—	—	—	11/13	11/20	11/27
Feb 5	9/25	10/ 2	10/ 9	10/16	10/23	—	—	—	11/20	11/27	12/ 4
Feb 12	10/ 2	10/ 9	10/16	10/23	10/30	—	—	—	11/27	12/ 4	12/11
Feb 19	10/ 9	10/16	10/23	10/30	11/ 6	—	—	—	12/ 4	12/11	12/18
Feb 26	—	10/23	10/30	11/ 6	11/13	11/20	—	—	12/11	12/18	12/25
Mar 5	—	10/30	11/ 6	11/13	11/20	11/27	—	—	12/18	12/25	1/ 1
Mar 12	—	11/ 6	11/13	11/20	11/27	12/ 4	—	—	12/25	1/ 1	1/ 8
Mar 19	—	11/13	11/20	11/27	12/ 4	12/11	—	—	1/ 1	1/ 8	1/15
Mar 26	—	11/20	11/27	12/ 4	12/11	12/18	—	—	1/ 8	1/15	1/22
Apr 2	—	—	12/ 4	12/11	12/18	12/25	1/ 1	—	1/15	1/22	1/29
Apr 9	—	—	12/11	12/18	12/25	1/ 1	1/ 8	—	1/22	1/29	2/ 5
Apr 16	—	—	12/18	12/25	1/ 1	1/ 8	1/15	—	1/29	2/ 5	2/12
Apr 23	—	—	12/25	1/ 1	1/ 8	1/15	1/22	—	2/ 5	2/12	2/19
Apr 30	—	—	—	1/ 8	1/15	1/22	1/29	2/ 5	2/12	2/19	2/26
May 7	—	—	—	1/15	1/22	1/29	2/ 5	2/12	2/19	2/26	3/ 5
May 14	—	—	—	1/22	1/29	2/ 5	2/12	2/19	2/26	3/ 5	3/12
May 21	—	—	—	1/29	2/ 5	2/12	2/19	2/26	3/ 5	3/12	3/19
May 28	—	—	—	—	—	2/19	2/26	3/ 5	3/12	3/19	3/26
Jun 4	—	—	—	—	—	2/26	3/ 5	3/12	3/19	3/26	4/ 2
Jun 11	—	—	—	—	—	3/ 5	3/12	3/19	3/26	4/ 2	4/ 9
Jun 18	—	—	—	—	—	3/12	3/19	3/26	4/ 2	4/ 9	4/16
Jun 25	—	—	—	—	—	3/19	3/26	4/ 2	4/ 9	4/16	4/23
Jul 2	—	—	—	—	—	3/26	4/ 2	4/ 9	4/16	4/23	4/30
Jul 9	—	—	—	—	—	4/ 2	4/ 9	4/16	4/23	4/30	5/ 7
Jul 16	—	—	—	—	—	4/ 9	4/16	4/23	4/30	5/ 7	5/14
Jul 23	—	—	—	—	—	4/16	4/23	4/30	5/ 7	5/14	5/21
Jul 30	—	—	—	—	—	4/23	4/30	5/ 7	5/14	5/21	5/28
Aug 6	—	—	—	—	—	4/30	5/ 7	5/14	5/21	5/28	6/ 4
Aug 13	—	—	—	—	—	5/ 7	5/14	5/21	5/28	6/ 4	6/11
Aug 20	—	—	—	—	—	5/14	5/21	5/28	6/ 4	6/11	6/18
Aug 27	—	—	—	—	—	5/21	5/28	6/ 4	6/11	6/18	6/25
Sep 3	—	—	—	—	—	5/28	6/ 4	6/11	6/18	6/25	7/ 2
Sep 10	—	—	—	—	—	6/ 4	6/11	6/18	6/25	7/ 2	7/ 9
Sep 17	—	—	—	—	—	6/11	6/18	6/25	7/ 2	7/ 9	7/16
Sep 24	—	—	—	—	—	6/18	6/25	7/ 2	7/ 9	7/16	7/23

(Continued)

Fig. 4—6

the period between succeeding crops. In this example it was desired to have a crop of standard mums about weekly, and this is possible with a 15-bench area with single-stem culture.

After the rotation chart is made, schedule sheets (Fig. 4-7) for

Chrysanthemum Cut Flower Scheduling Table (Cont'd)

Flowering Date	Planting Dates								Start-of-Short-Day Dates		
	19	18	17	16	15	14	13	12	11	10	9
Oct 1	—	—	—	—	6/18	6/25	7/ 2	7/ 9	7/16	7/23	7/30
Oct 8	—	—	—	—	6/25	7/ 2	7/ 9	7/16	7/23	7/30	8/ 6
Oct 15	—	—	—	—	7/ 2	7/ 9	7/16	7/23	7/30	8/ 6	8/13
Oct 22	—	—	—	—	7/ 9	7/16	7/23	7/30	8/ 6	8/13	8/20
Oct 29	—	—	7/ 2	7/ 9	7/16	7/23	7/30	—	8/13	8/20	8/27
Nov 5	—	—	7/ 9	7/16	7/23	7/30	8/ 6	—	8/20	8/27	9/ 3
Nov 12	—	—	7/16	7/23	7/30	8/ 6	8/13	—	8/27	9/ 3	9/10
Nov 19	—	—	7/23	7/30	8/ 6	8/13	8/20	—	9/ 3	9/10	9/17
Nov 26	—	7/23	7/30	8/ 6	8/13	8/20	—	—	9/10	9/17	9/24
Dec 3	—	7/30	8/ 6	8/13	8/20	8/27	—	—	9/17	9/24	10/ 1
Dec 10	—	8/ 6	8/13	8/20	8/27	9/ 3	—	—	9/24	10/ 1	10/ 8
Dec 17	—	8/13	8/20	8/27	9/ 3	9/10	—	—	10/ 1	10/ 8	10/15
Dec 24	—	8/20	8/27	9/ 3	9/10	9/17	—	—	10/ 8	10/15	10/22
Dec 31	8/20	8/27	9/ 3	9/10	9/17	—	—	—	10/15	10/22	10/29
Jan 7	8/27	9/ 3	9/10	9/17	9/24	—	—	—	10/22	10/29	11/ 5
Jan 14	9/ 3	9/10	9/17	9/24	10/ 1	—	—	—	10/29	11/ 5	11/12
Jan 21	9/10	9/17	9/24	10/ 1	10/ 8	—	—	—	11/ 5	11/12	11/19
Jan 28	9/17	9/24	10/ 1	10/ 8	10/15	—	—	—	11/12	11/19	11/26
Feb 4	9/24	10/ 1	10/ 8	10/15	10/22	—	—	—	11/19	11/26	12/ 3
Feb 11	10/ 1	10/ 8	10/15	10/22	10/29	—	—	—	11/26	12/ 3	12/10
Feb 18	10/ 8	10/15	10/22	10/29	11/ 5	—	—	—	12/ 3	12/10	12/17
Feb 25	—	10/22	10/29	11/ 5	11/12	11/19	—	—	12/10	12/17	12/24
Mar 4	—	10/29	11/ 5	11/12	11/19	11/26	—	—	12/17	12/24	12/31
Mar 11	—	11/ 5	11/12	11/19	11/26	12/ 3	—	—	12/24	12/31	1/ 7
Mar 18	—	11/12	11/19	11/26	12/ 3	12/10	—	—	12/31	1/ 7	1/14
Mar 25	—	11/19	11/26	12/ 3	12/10	12/17	—	—	1/ 7	1/14	1/21
Apr 1	—	—	12/ 3	12/10	12/17	12/24	12/31	—	1/14	1/21	1/28
Apr 8	—	—	12/10	12/17	12/24	12/31	1/ 7	—	1/21	1/28	2/ 4
Apr 15	—	—	12/17	12/24	12/31	1/ 7	1/14	—	1/28	2/ 4	2/11
Apr 22	—	—	12/24	12/31	1/ 7	1/14	1/21	—	2/ 4	2/11	2/18
Apr 29	—	—	—	1/ 7	1/14	1/21	1/28	2/ 4	2/11	2/18	2/25
May 6	—	—	—	1/14	1/21	1/28	2/ 4	2/11	2/18	2/25	3/ 4
May 13	—	—	—	1/21	1/28	2/ 4	2/11	2/18	2/25	3/ 4	3/11
May 20	—	—	—	1/28	2/ 4	2/11	2/18	2/25	3/ 4	3/11	3/18
May 27	—	—	—	—	—	2/18	2/25	3/ 4	3/11	3/18	3/25
Jun 3	—	—	—	—	—	2/25	3/ 4	3/11	3/18	3/25	4/ 1
Jun 10	—	—	—	—	—	3/ 4	3/11	3/18	3/25	4/ 1	4/ 8
Jun 17	—	—	—	—	—	3/11	3/18	3/25	4/ 1	4/ 8	4/15
Jun 24	—	—	—	—	—	3/18	3/25	4/ 1	4/ 8	4/15	4/22

Fig. 4—6 (Cont'd)

each planting can be made that give the quantity of each variety being planted, planting date, start of short days, and flowering date.

Pot Plant Rotations

Rotations for pot plants are usually more complex than those for

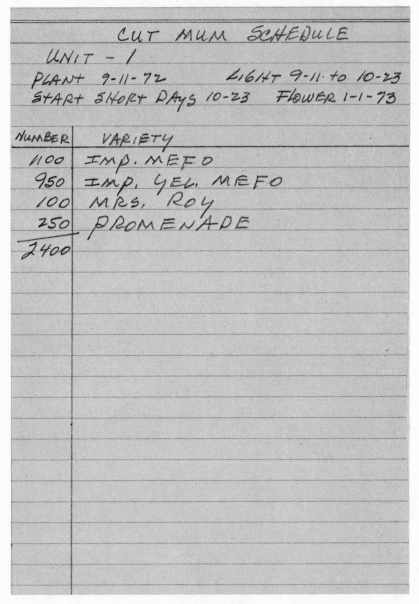

CUT MUM SCHEDULE

UNIT - 1

PLANT 9-11-72   LIGHT 9-11 to 10-23

START SHORT DAYS 10-23   FLOWER 1-1-73

NUMBER	VARIETY
1100	IMP. MEFO
950	IMP. YEL. MEFO
100	MRS. ROY
250	PROMENADE
2400	

Fig. 4—7. A reproduction of the chrysanthemum foreman's first schedule sheet. The planting date, start-of-short-days date, and flowering date were obtained from the scheduling table (Fig. 4—6) by using the variety classification from Fig. 4—4. Promenade will flower about one week earlier than the other varieties, but this is not of consequence in this year-round program.

cut flowers. More planning is required. The plants can and must be spaced as they develop. The area for spacing won't be available unless the rotation is carefully planned and then closely followed. The good rotation will provide the kind and quality of plants for the potential market and utilize the greenhouse space as fully as possible (Fig. 4-8).

At the same time the market is being evaluated, transportation of the plants must be given consideration. Will the customer make pick-ups, or will the plants be delivered or shipped?

Although the rotation will be in terms of square feet of bench space, the record must indicate how the plants are placed on the bench —number of plants across the bench and number of rows down the bench—, as well as the total number of plants of a kind and size that each bench will hold.

The market evaluation in this example indicates that there is a good demand from retail flower shops year-round for pot mums and azaleas within a 50-mile radius of the greenhouse. Some customers would make pick-up, but most of the plants would have to be delivered. The demand for holiday plants is about equally divided between retail flower shops and markets other than flower shops. Practically all of these plants would have to be delivered. The holiday crops produced would be pot mums for Thanksgiving; poinsettias and azaleas for Christmas; pot mums, azaleas, tulips, and hyacinths for Valentine's Day (Fig. 4-9); pot mums, lilies (Fig. 4-10), azaleas, and hydrangeas for Easter; pot mums, gloxinias and hydrangeas for Mother's Day; and pot mums for Memorial Day. Gloxinias would be forced during the summer, and 2¼-inch poinsettias would be produced for sale in summer and fall.

The azaleas to be forced from December through April would be from growing-on plants started in polyethylene film houses in May (Fig. 4-11). The poly film would be replaced with saran screen during the summer, and then the houses re-covered with poly film again in the fall. The azaleas would be brought in from these houses for forcing during the winter as needed. The azaleas to be forced from May through November would be budded plants shipped in weekly from an azalea specialist.

To produce the poinsettia cuttings required, cuttings would be

POT PLANT ROTATION — SPACE OCCUPIED (SQ. FT.)

CROP	JAN	FEB	MAR	APR	MAY	JUN	JUL	AUG	SEP	OCT	NOV	DEC
YR-RD MUMS	8625	8625	8625	8625	8625	8625	8625	8625	8625	8625	8625	7125
YR-RD AZALEAS	4125	3375	1500	375	7125	7125	7125	7125	7125	7125	4875	4500
POINSETTIAS	—	—	—	—	7875	19125	19125	26625	24750	16875	22125	22250
HOLIDAY AZALEAS	375	375	1875	1875	—	—	—	—	—	—	1875	1875
HOLIDAY MUMS	8625	12750	20250	21375	17250	—	—	—	5625	5625	5250	2625
TULIPS	375	375	—									
HYACINTHS	375	375	—									
LILIES	8750	8750	3750	3750								
HYDRANGEAS	5625	5625	7500	7500	1875							
GLOXINIAS	—	750	1500	1500	2250	2250	1500	1500	750			
TOTALS	31875	36000	45000	45000	45000	37125	36375	43875	43875	35250	42750	42375

Fig. 4—8. A reproduction of the pot plant foreman's rotation sheet. Total available space is 45,000 square feet This chart indicates how this space is being utilized.

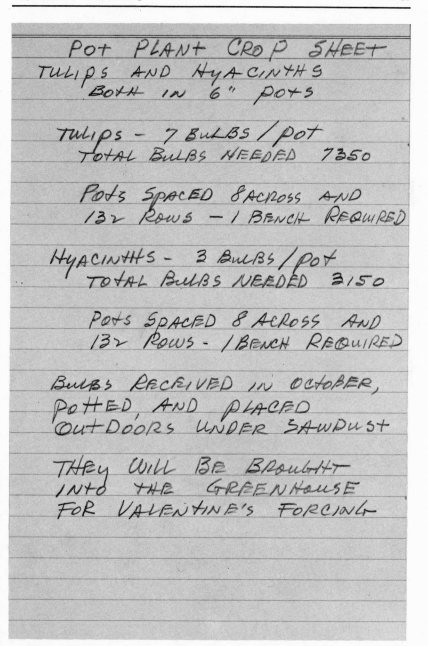

POT PLANT CROP SHEET
TULIPS AND HYACINTHS
BOTH IN 6" POTS

TULIPS - 7 BULBS / POT
TOTAL BULBS NEEDED 7350

POTS SPACED 8 ACROSS AND
132 ROWS - 1 BENCH REQUIRED

HYACINTHS - 3 BULBS / POT
TOTAL BULBS NEEDED 3150

POTS SPACED 8 ACROSS AND
132 ROWS - 1 BENCH REQUIRED

BULBS RECEIVED IN OCTOBER,
POTTED, AND PLACED
OUTDOORS UNDER SAWDUST

THEY WILL BE BROUGHT
INTO THE GREENHOUSE
FOR VALENTINE'S FORCING

Fig. 4—9. A reproduction of the pot plant foreman's crop sheet for tulips and hyacinths. The crop sheet gives general handling and bulb and space requirements.

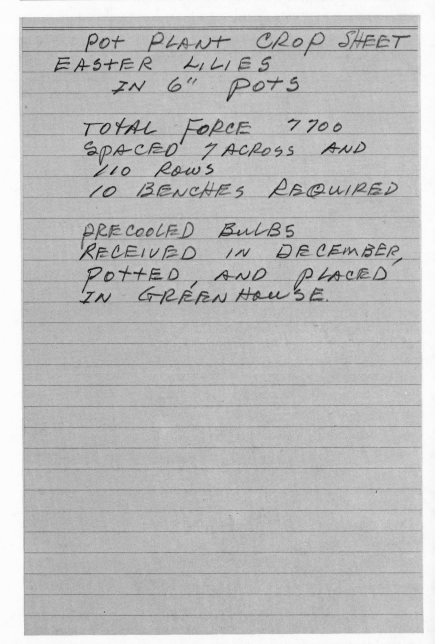

POT PLANT CROP SHEET
EASTER LILIES
    IN 6" POTS

TOTAL FORCE 7700
SPACED 7 ACROSS AND
110 ROWS
10 BENCHES REQUIRED

PRECOOLED BULBS
RECEIVED IN DECEMBER,
POTTED, AND PLACED
IN GREENHOUSE.

Fig. 4—10. A reproduction of the pot plant foreman's crop sheet for Easter lilies. The crop sheet gives the bulb and space requirements for the crop.

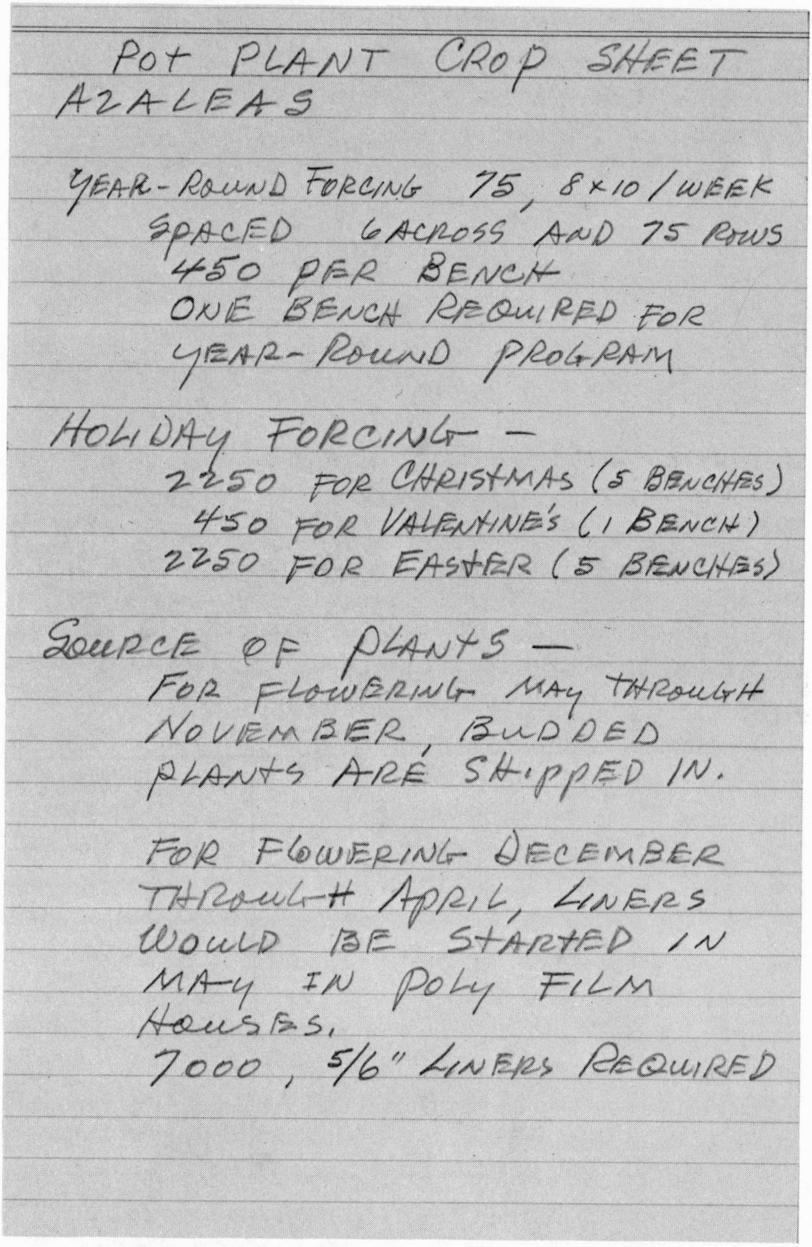

POT PLANT CROP SHEET
AZALEAS

YEAR-ROUND FORCING 75, 8×10 / WEEK
SPACED 6 ACROSS AND 75 ROWS
450 PER BENCH
ONE BENCH REQUIRED FOR
YEAR-ROUND PROGRAM

HOLIDAY FORCING —
2250 FOR CHRISTMAS (5 BENCHES)
450 FOR VALENTINE'S (1 BENCH)
2250 FOR EASTER (5 BENCHES)

SOURCE OF PLANTS —
FOR FLOWERING MAY THROUGH
NOVEMBER, BUDDED
PLANTS ARE SHIPPED IN.

FOR FLOWERING DECEMBER
THROUGH APRIL, LINERS
WOULD BE STARTED IN
MAY IN POLY FILM
HOUSES.
7000, 5/6" LINERS REQUIRED

Fig. 4—11. A reproduction of the pot plant foreman's crop sheet for azaleas. The crop sheet gives the general plan for azaleas and the plant and space requirements.

shipped in from California in May and June for stock plants. The cuttings produced on these stock plants would be rooted in 2¼-inch pots and sold as 2¼-inch plants or panned for flowering plant production (Fig. 4-12).

The hydrangea plants would be forced from budded plants shipped in from the hydrangea specialist in December-January (Fig. 4-13).

For the gloxinia production, 2¼-inch gloxinia seedling plants would be used (Fig. 4-14).

Most pot plants growers attempt to produce the maximum number of plants in their greenhouses for Christmas and the spring holidays, and this makes an almost natural rotation between those crops —except some fitting is required. The variable date of Easter causes an equally variable date for starting the plants, but within limits the Easter plants can be started in the greenhouse after the poinsettia crop is shipped for Christmas. Mother's Day rotates fairly well with Valentine's Day except that the demand for plants is greater for Mother's Day. There usually is no good answer for producing these extra plants for Mother's Day other than spacing the plants closer together until after the Easter crop is shipped out or using temporary houses of some kind. In the rotation that is used here, actually the extra space for the Mother's Day plants is the result of rotating that crop partially with the natural-season azaleas in the polyethylene houses. This provides the expansion needed at that time of the year.

There is no one answer for keeping the pot plant range in full production during the summer. In past years natural-season chrysanthemums were often used in the rotation. The primary reasons this procedure is not so popular now is that it is not so economical to rotate between pot crops and cut flower crops—too many physical adjustments need to be made, and there has often been an over-supply of natural-season chrysanthemums in the fall, with resulting depressed prices. In the rotation used here the area would be kept working during the summer by producing gloxinias and 2¼-inch poinsettias.

This pot plant range (Fig. 4-8) would consist of two ridge and furrow glasshouse areas and six separate quonset-type polyethylene houses, each 22 feet by 90 feet. The glasshouses would have 5-foot ✕

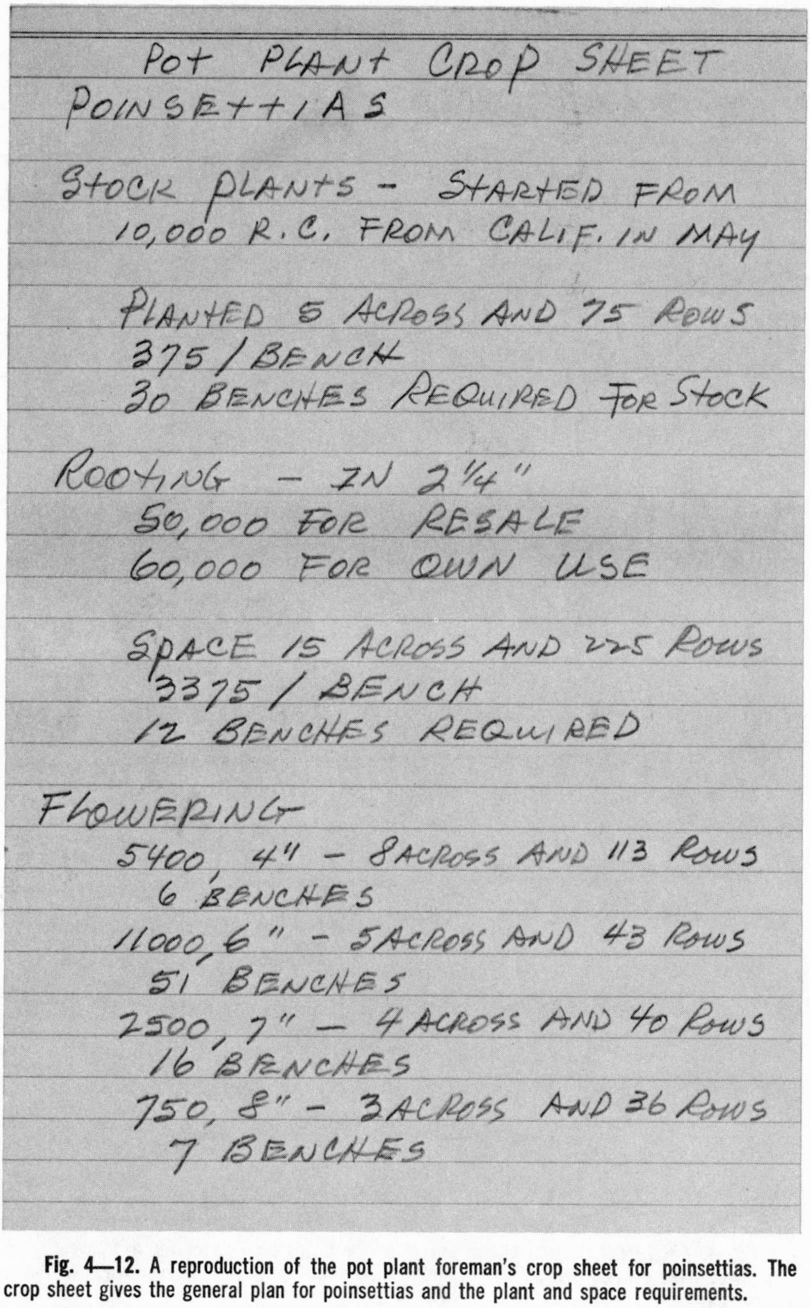

Pot PLANt CROP SHEET
POINSETTIAS

Stock PLANtS - STARTED FROM
  10,000 R.C. FROM CALIF. IN MAY

PLANTED 5 ACROSS AND 75 ROWS
  375 / BENCH
  30 BENCHES REQUIRED For Stock

ROOTING - IN 2¼"
  50,000 FOR RESALE
  60,000 FOR OWN USE

SPACE 15 ACROSS AND 225 ROWS
  3375 / BENCH
  12 BENCHES REQUIRED

FLOWERING
  5400, 4" - 8 ACROSS AND 113 ROWS
    6 BENCHES
  11000, 6" - 5 ACROSS AND 43 ROWS
    51 BENCHES
  2500, 7" - 4 ACROSS AND 40 ROWS
    16 BENCHES
  750, 8" - 3 ACROSS AND 36 ROWS
    7 BENCHES

Fig. 4—12. A reproduction of the pot plant foreman's crop sheet for poinsettias. The crop sheet gives the general plan for poinsettias and the plant and space requirements.

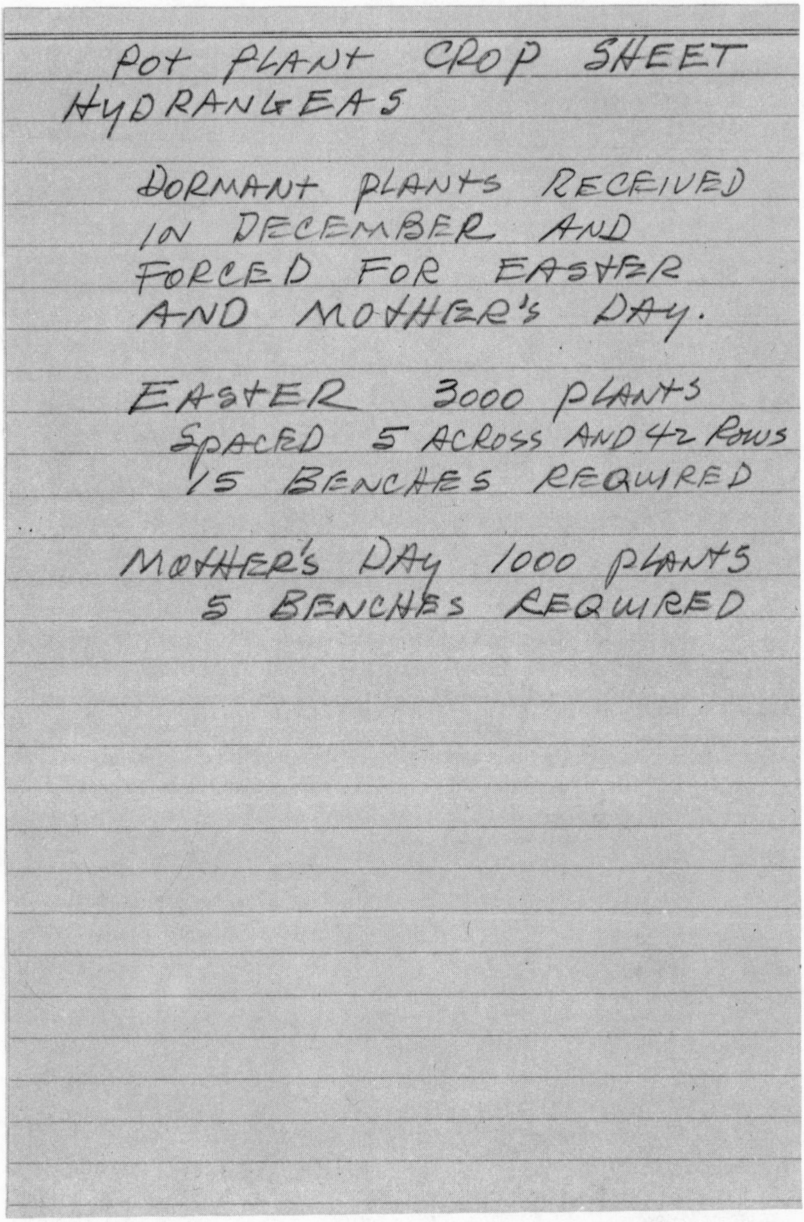

> POT PLANT CROP SHEET
> HYDRANGEAS
>
> DORMANT PLANTS RECEIVED
> IN DECEMBER AND
> FORCED FOR EASTER
> AND MOTHER's DAY.
>
> EASTER   3000 PLANTS
>   SPACED 5 ACROSS AND 42 ROWS
>   15 BENCHES REQUIRED
>
> MOTHER's DAY 1000 PLANTS
>   5 BENCHES REQUIRED

Fig. 4—13. A reproduction of the pot plant foreman's crop sheet for hydrangeas. The crop sheet gives general plan and plant and space requirements for the Easter and Mother's Day hydrangeas.

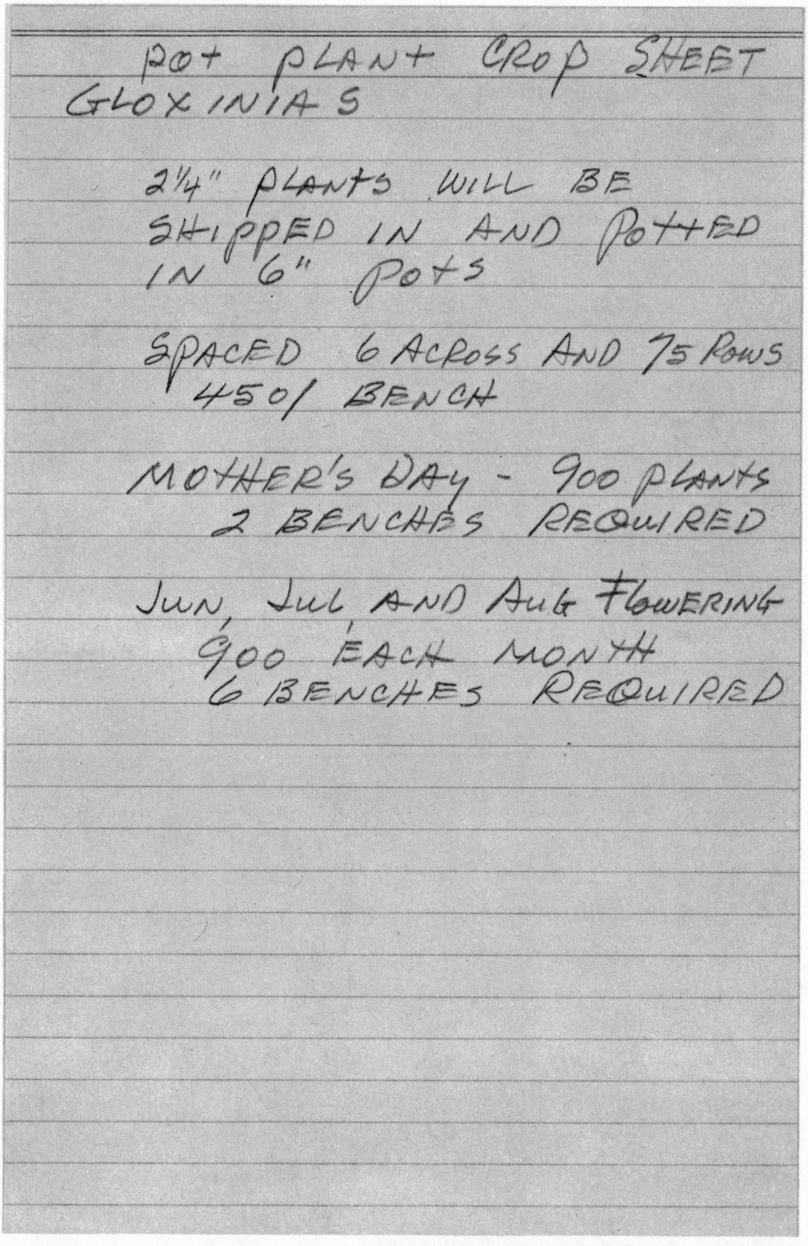

Pot plant Crop Sheet
GLOXINIAS

2¼" plants will be
shipped in and potted
in 6" pots

Spaced 6 Across and 75 Rows
450/ Bench

Mother's Day - 900 plants
2 Benches Required

Jun, Jul and Aug Flowering
900 each month
6 Benches Required

Fig. 4—14. A reproduction of the pot plant foreman's crop sheet for gloxinias. The crop sheet gives the general plan and plant and space requirements for gloxinias.

75-foot benches, and the poly houses have 5-foot × 75-foot beds. The glasshouses would be approximately 22 feet × 160 feet, with a central walk through the houses. One ridge and furrow area would be nine houses, and the other eight houses. For the entire area this would make a total of 102 benches and 18 beds, each 5 feet × 75 feet, 375 square feet per bench or bed and a total growing area for the range of 45,000 square feet. As the area utilization (rotation) chart illustrates, the total growing area would be well occupied during the year. Of the space that is not occupied in January and February, 3,000 square feet in January and 13,125 square feet of it in February would be in the poly houses. There is some possibility that bulbs could be forced in this period, but the market should be surveyed first. All of the area that is not occupied in November and December would be in the poly houses that had been partially vacated by moving azalea plants to the glasshouses for forcing.

A double-number timing classification system for pot mums (Fig. 4-15) was developed for presentation here. It is very similar to the one used for cut mums, discussed earlier. The first number is the total crop time, and the second number is the number of weeks of short days. The planting date and start-of-short-days date for any given flowering date can be determined readily by inspection of the scheduling table (Fig. 4-16). On the flowering date line, the planting date is located in the column headed by the first number of the timing classification and the start-of-short-days date is in the column headed by the second number of the classification.

Varieties that have the same timing classification double number will flower at the same time and at about the same height. For flowering during the summer the Mountains and Mandalays may be handled in the same way, but Illini Trophy should be planted a week later. Actually on year-round pot mum programs (Fig. 4-17) there is not much concern if the date of flowering varies by a week because there is a continuous supply of all varieties in spite of the entire planting not being ready for sale at the same time. Holiday crops, however, must be flowered exactly on schedule for the holiday, and they must be planted at the right time for that date (Fig. 4-19 and Fig. 4-20).

The flexibility of the double-number timing classification system

Pot Chrysanthemum Timing Classification

Classification for Month of Flowering

Variety	Jan	Feb	Mar	Apr	May	Jun	Jul	Aug	Sep	Oct	Nov	Dec
Always Pink	11-8	11-8	11-8	11-8	10-8	10-8	10-8	10-8	10-8	10-8	11-8	11-8
Winter Carnival	11-9	11-9	11-9	10-9	—	—	—	—	—	10-9	10-9	11-9
Marguerita 773	—	—	—	10-9	10-9	10-9	10-9	10-9	10-9	10-9	—	—
Imp. Yel. Marguerita	—	—	—	10-9	10-9	10-9	10-9	10-9	10-9	10-9	—	—
Wild Honey	—	—	—	—	10-9	10-9	10-9	10-9	10-9	10-9	—	—
Wildfire	—	—	—	—	10-9	10-9	10-9	10-9	10-9	10-9	—	—
Dramatic	11-9	11-9	11-9	10-9	10-9	10-9	10-9	10-9	10-9	10-9	10-9	11-9
Distinctive	—	—	—	9-8	9-8	9-8	10-9	10-9	10-9	10-9	—	—
Puritan	11-9	11-9	11-9	11-9	11-9	10-9	11-10	11-10	11-10	10-9	11-9	11-9
Paragon	11-9	11-9	11-9	10-8	10-8	—	—	—	—	10-9	11-9	11-9
Yel. Puritan	12-10	12-10	11-9	11-9	11-9	10-9	10-9	10-9	10-9	10-9	11-9	11-9
Yel. Paragon	11-9	11-9	11-9	10-8	10-8	—	—	—	—	10-9	11-9	11-9
Illini Trophy	11-9	11-9	11-9	11-9	11-9	10-9	10-9	10-9	10-9	10-9	11-9	11-9
Glo Pink	11-9	11-9	11-9	11-9	11-9	10-9	10-9	10-9	10-9	10-9	11-9	11-9
Deep Conquest	11-9	11-9	11-9	11-9	11-9	—	—	—	10-9	10-9	11-9	11-9
Malabar	11-9	11-9	11-9	11-9	11-9	10-9	10-9	10-9	10-9	10-9	11-9	11-9
Neptune	12-9	12-9	12-9	12-9	12-9	11-9	11-9	11-9	11-9	11-9	12-9	12-9
Yel. Torch	—	—	—	—	—	—	11-9	11-9	11-9	—	—	—
Red Torch	12-9	12-9	12-9	12-9	12-9	11-9	11-9	11-9	11-9	11-9	12-9	12-9
Matador	12-9	12-9	12-9	12-9	12-9	11-9	11-9	11-9	11-9	11-9	12-9	12-9
Deep Mermaid	—	—	—	12-9	12-9	11-9	11-9	11-9	11-9	11-9	12-9	—
Bonnie Jean	—	—	—	11-10	11-10	11-10	11-10	11-10	11-10	11-10	—	—
Snow Crystal	12-10	12-10	12-10	11-10	11-10	11-10	11-10	11-10	11-10	11-10	11-10	12-10
Cr. Yel. Prin. Anne	12-10	12-10	12-10	11-10	11-10	11-10	11-10	11-10	11-10	11-10	11-10	12-10
Brt. Gold. Anne	12-10	12-10	12-10	11-10	11-10	11-10	11-10	11-10	11-10	11-10	11-10	12-10
Gold. Crystal	12-10	12-10	12-10	11-10	11-10	11-10	11-10	11-10	11-10	11-10	11-10	12-10
Imp. Yel. Bonnie Jean	—	—	—	11-10	11-10	11-10	11-10	11-10	11-10	11-10	—	—
XR Br. Prin. Anne	12-10	12-10	12-10	11-10	11-10	—	—	—	—	11-10	11-10	12-10
Copper Anne	12-10	12-10	12-10	11-10	11-10	—	—	—	—	11-10	11-10	12-10
Red Anne	12-10	12-10	12-10	11-10	—	—	—	—	—	11-10	11-10	12-10
Aglow	12-10	12-10	12-10	11-10	11-10	11-10	—	—	—	11-10	11-10	12-10
Deep Tuneful	12-10	12-10	12-10	11-10	11-10	11-10	—	—	—	11-10	11-10	12-10
Prin. Anne Superb	12-10	12-10	12-10	11-10	—	—	—	—	—	11-10	11-10	12-10
Regal Anne	12-10	12-10	12-10	11-10	—	—	—	—	—	11-10	11-10	12-10
Mountain Snow	—	—	12-10	12-10	12-10	11-10	11-10	11-10	11-10	11-10	12-10	—
Mountain Sun	—	—	12-10	12-10	12-10	11-10	11-10	11-10	11-10	11-10	12-10	—
Goldstar	—	—	—	—	12-10	12-10	11-10	11-10	11-10	11-10	12-10	—
Redcap	12-10	12-10	12-10	12-10	12-10	11-10	11-10	11-10	11-10	11-10	12-10	12-10
Maritime	—	—	—	12-10	12-10	11-10	11-10	11-10	11-10	11-10	—	—
Sunny Mandalay	—	—	13-10	13-10	13-10	12-10	11-10	11-10	11-10	12-10	13-10	—
Sparkling Mandalay	—	—	13-10	13-10	13-10	12-10	11-10	11-10	11-10	12-10	13-10	—
Glowing Mandalay	—	—	13-10	13-10	13-10	12-10	11-10	11-10	11-10	12-10	13-10	—
Copper Bowl	13-10	13-10	13-10	13-10	13-10	12-10	12-10	12-10	12-10	12-10	13-10	13-10
Orange Bowl	—	—	—	13-10	13-10	12-10	12-10	12-10	12-10	12-10	—	—
White Ann	13-11	13-11	13-11	12-11	12-11	12-11	12-11	12-11	12-11	12-11	12-11	13-11

Fig. 4—15

Pot Chrysanthemum Scheduling Table

Flowering Date	Planting Dates		Start-of-Short-Day Dates			
	13	12	11	10	9	8
Jan 1	10/ 2	10/ 9	10/16	10/23	10/30	11/ 6
Jan 8	10/ 9	10/16	10/23	10/30	11/ 6	11/13
Jan 15	10/16	10/23	10/30	11/ 6	11/13	11/20
Jan 22	10/23	10/30	11/ 6	11/13	11/20	11/27
Jan 29	10/30	11/ 6	11/13	11/20	11/27	12/ 4
Feb 5	11/ 6	11/13	11/20	11/27	12/ 4	12/11
Feb 12	11/13	11/20	11/27	12/ 4	12/11	12/18
Feb 19	11/20	11/27	12/ 4	12/11	12/18	12/25
Feb 26	11/27	12/ 4	12/11	12/18	12/25	1/ 1
Mar 5	12/ 4	12/11	12/18	12/25	1/ 1	1/ 8
Mar 12	12/11	12/18	12/25	1/ 1	1/ 8	1/15
Mar 19	12/18	12/25	1/ 1	1/ 8	1/15	1/22
Mar 26	12/25	1/ 1	1/ 8	1/15	1/22	1/29
Apr 2	1/ 1	1/ 8	1/15	1/22	1/29	2/ 5
Apr 9	1/ 8	1/15	1/22	1/29	2/ 5	2/12
Apr 16	1/15	1/22	1/29	2/ 5	2/12	2/19
Apr 23	1/22	1/29	2/ 5	2/12	2/19	2/26
Apr 30	1/29	2/ 5	2/12	2/19	2/26	3/ 5
May 7	2/ 5	2/12	2/19	2/26	3/ 5	3/12
May 14	2/12	2/19	2/26	3/ 5	3/12	3/19
May 21	2/19	2/26	3/ 5	3/12	3/19	3/26
May 28	2/26	3/ 5	3/12	3/19	3/26	4/ 2
Jun 4	—	3/12	3/19	3/26	4/ 2	4/ 9
Jun 11	—	3/19	3/26	4/ 2	4/ 9	4/16
Jun 18	—	3/26	4/ 2	4/ 9	4/16	4/23
Jun 25	—	4/ 2	4/ 9	4/16	4/23	4/30
Jul 2	—	4/ 9	4/16	4/23	4/30	5/ 7
Jul 9	—	4/16	4/23	4/30	5/ 7	5/14
Jul 16	—	4/23	4/30	5/ 7	5/14	5/21
Jul 23	—	4/30	5/ 7	5/14	5/21	5/28
Jul 30	—	5/ 7	5/14	5/21	5/28	6/ 4
Aug 6	—	5/14	5/21	5/28	6/ 4	6/11
Aug 13	—	5/21	5/28	6/ 4	6/11	6/18
Aug 20	—	5/28	6/ 4	6/11	6/18	6/25
Aug 27	—	6/ 4	6/11	6/18	6/25	7/ 2
Sep 3	—	6/11	6/18	6/25	7/ 2	7/ 9
Sep 10	—	6/18	6/25	7/ 2	7/ 9	7/16
Sep 17	—	6/25	7/ 2	7/ 9	7/16	7/23
Sep 24	—	7/ 2	7/ 9	7/16	7/23	7/30

(Continued)

Fig. 4—16

Pot Chrysanthemum Scheduling Table (Cont'd)

Flowering Date	Planting Dates		Start-of-Short-Day Dates			
	13	12	11	10	9	8
Oct 1	—	7/ 9	7/16	7/23	7/30	8/ 6
Oct 8	—	7/16	7/23	7/30	8/ 6	8/13
Oct 15	—	7/23	7/30	8/ 6	8/13	8/20
Oct 22	—	7/30	8/ 6	8/13	8/20	8/27
Oct 29	7/30	8/ 6	8/13	8/20	8/27	9/ 3
Nov 5	8/ 6	8/13	8/20	8/27	9/ 3	9/10
Nov 12	8/13	8/20	8/27	9/ 3	9/10	9/17
Nov 19	8/20	8/27	9/ 3	9/10	9/17	9/24
Nov 26	8/27	9/ 3	9/10	9/17	9/24	10/ 1
Dec 3	9/ 3	9/10	9/17	9/24	10/ 1	10/ 8
Dec 10	9/10	9/17	9/24	10/ 1	10/ 8	10/15
Dec 17	9/17	9/24	10/ 1	10/ 8	10/15	10/22
Dec 24	9/24	10/ 1	10/ 8	10/15	10/22	10/29
Dec 31	10/ 1	10/ 8	10/15	10/22	10/29	11/ 5
Jan 7	10/ 8	10/15	10/22	10/29	11/ 5	11/12
Jan 14	10/15	10/22	10/29	11/ 5	11/12	11/19
Jan 21	10/11	10/29	11/ 5	11/12	11/19	11/26
Jan 28	10/29	11/ 5	11/12	11/19	11/26	12/ 3
Feb 4	11/ 5	11/12	11/19	11/26	12/ 3	12/10
Feb 11	11/12	11/19	11/26	12/ 3	12/10	12/17
Feb 18	11/19	11/26	12/ 3	12/10	12/17	12/24
Feb 25	11/26	12/ 3	12/10	12/17	12/24	12/31
Mar 4	12/ 3	12/10	12/17	12/24	12/31	1/ 7
Mar 11	12/10	12/17	12/24	12/31	1/ 7	1/14
Mar 18	12/17	12/24	12/31	1/ 7	1/14	1/21
Mar 25	12/24	12/31	1/ 7	1/14	1/21	1/28
Apr 1	12/31	1/ 7	1/14	1/21	1/28	2/ 4
Apr 8	1/ 7	1/14	1/21	1/28	2/ 4	2/11
Apr 15	1/14	1/21	1/28	2/ 4	2/11	2/18
Apr 22	1/21	1/28	2/ 4	2/11	2/18	2/25
Apr 29	1/28	2/ 4	2/11	2/18	2/25	3/ 4
May 6	2/ 4	2/11	2/18	2/25	3/ 4	3/11
May 13	2/11	2/18	2/25	3/ 4	3/11	3/18
May 20	2/18	2/25	3/ 4	3/11	3/18	3/25
May 27	2/25	3/ 4	3/11	3/18	3/25	4/ 1
Jun 3	—	3/11	3/18	3/25	4/ 1	4/ 8
Jun 10	—	3/18	3/25	4/ 1	4/ 8	4/15
Jun 17	—	3/25	4/ 1	4/ 8	4/15	4/22
Jun 24	—	4/ 1	4/ 8	4/15	4/22	4/29

Fig. 4—16 (Cont'd)

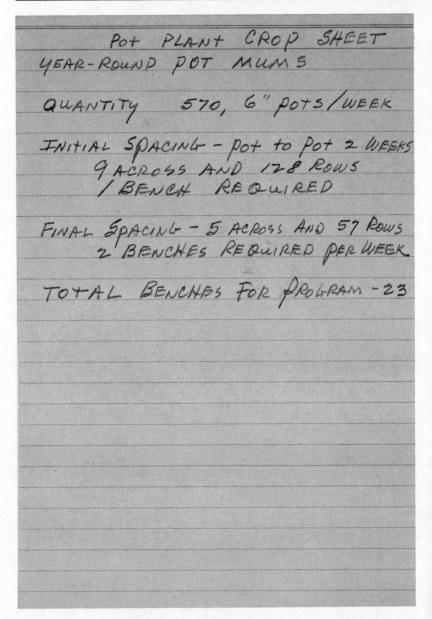

Pot PLANt CROP SHEET
YEAR-ROUND POT MUMS

QUANTITY   570, 6" POTS/WEEK

INITIAL SPACING - pot to pot 2 WEEKS
        9 ACROSS AND 128 ROWS
        / BENCH REQUIRED

FINAL SPACING - 5 ACROSS AND 57 ROWS
        2 BENCHES REQUIRED PER WEEK

TOTAL BENCHES FOR PROGRAM -23

Fig. 4—17. A reproduction of the pot plant foreman's crop sheet for pot mums. This gives the general method of handling the year-round pot mum program and the space requirements.

	Pot mum SCHEDULE			
PLANT 10-16-72		PINCH 10-30		
NUMBER	VARIETY	LIGHT	SHADE	FLOWER
500	PARAGON	10-16	10-30	1-1-73
1850	YEL. PARAGON			
200	RED TORCH		11-6	1-8-73
300	ILL. TROPHY		10-30	1-1-73
2850				

Fig. 4—18. A reproduction of the pot plant foreman's pot mum schedule for one week. The planting date, start-of-short-days (shade) date, and flowering date came from the schedule table (Fig. 4—16) and use of the variety classification number from Fig. 4—15. A schedule would be made for each planting date. The difference in the flowering date of Red Torch is not of concern because this is a year-round program.

POT PLANT CROP SHEET
HOLIDAY POT MUMS
FINISH SPACING - 5 ACROSS AND
57 ROWS - 285/ BENCH

THANKSGIVING 2000 - 7 BENCHES

VALENTINE'S 2000 - 7 BENCHES

EASTER 5000 - 17 BENCHES

MOTHER'S DAY 10,000 — 35 BENCHES

DECORATION DAY 3000 - 11 BENCHES

MOTHER'S DAY AND
DECORATION DAY CROPS
WILL BE STARTED IN
THE POLY FILM HOUSES.

Fig. 4—19. A reproduction of the pot plant foreman's crop sheet for holiday pot mums. The crop sheet gives the general plan and space requirements for the holiday pot mums.

EASTER POT MUM SCHEDULE

PLANT 1-15-73 PINCH 1-29

NUMBER	VARIETY	LIGHT	SHADE	FLOWER
7000	SUNNY MANDALAY	1-15	2-5	4-16
500	ORANGE BOWL	|	|	|
7500				

EASTER POT MUM SCHEDULE

PLANT 1-29-73 PINCH 2-12

NUMBER	VARIETY	LIGHT	SHADE	FLOWER
5000	PURITAN	1-29	2-12	4-16
2000	GLO PINK	|	|	|
9000	BRT. GOLD ANNE	|	2-5	|
500	ZR BR. P.A.	|	|	|
1000	PRIN. ANNE SUP.	|	|	|
17500				

Fig. 4—20. A reproduction of the pot plant foreman's Easter pot mum schedule sheets. The holiday pot plants must be timed to flower just right for the holiday. The pot mum varieties must be planted and given short days at the correct time. This scheduling was done by reference to the variety timing classification (Fig. 4—15) and scheduling table (Fig. 4—16).

is particularly helpful with pot mums. There is more variability in the response with these varieties, and the double number is a workable method for handling it. Some of these examples are: Distinctive is a 9-week response (10-9) in the summer but 8-week (9-8) in the spring; Puritan is known as a 9-week variety but responds as a 10 in the summer (11-10); the Mandalays are short-growing varieties spring and fall (13-10) but during the summer are medium height growers (11-10); and the Bowls follow somewhat the same pattern, but in addition their response slows to 11 weeks during the summer (12-11). Some growers find the Mandalays and possibly some of the other varieties have a shorter response in the spring. Although this timing classification chart does not indicate this, each grower can make the adjustment in classification numbers very easily.

The scheduling table is universal in its use. No adjustment needs to be made to it. If the right timing classification number is used, the scheduling table indicates the proper dates for planting and start of short days.

Pot mum plants should be pinched when they have made from 1½ inches to 2 inches of new growth after potting. It will vary with the time of the year, other growing conditions, and growth characteristics of the variety; but some plants should be pinched in about 10 days, and in other situations or with other plants they may require more than two weeks of growth before pinching.

● RETAIL GREENHOUSE ROTATION AND SCHEDULING

The primary work of the retail greenhouse necessarily must be designing and selling flowers. The flower and plant production work that is done must be coordinated with and complementary to the selling. The production plans should be based on supplying the needs of the retail flower shop only. This means that continuous, small quantities of varied flowers need to be produced.

Potential market: The retail trade at this greenhouse would be expected to be typical—largely special occasion and holiday flowers throughout the year, with bedding plant and garden supply sales in late spring and through the summer. In cut flowers carnations, snapdragons, and chrysanthemums would be produced in as uniform

CROP ROTATION AND USE OF SPACE IN RETAIL GREENHOUSE

BENCH	JAN	FEB	MAR	APR	MAY	JUN	JUL	AUG	SEP	OCT	NOV	DEC
1-1+2	FOLIAGE PLANTS											
1-3-10	DISPLAY PLANTS				GARDEN STORE				DISPLAY PLANTS			
2-1	WORK BENCH											
2-2	LILY			GERANIUM		CUT MUMS				POINSETTIA		
2-3		POT MUMS		GERANIUM		CUT MUMS				POINSETTIA		
2-4	POT MUMS				BEDDING		CUT MUMS				POINSETTIA	
3-1-10	CUT MUMS											
4-1		CARNATIONS							SNAPDRAGONS			
4-2		CARNATIONS								SNAPDRAGONS		
4-3	SNAPDRAGONS				CARNATIONS							
4-4	SNAPDRAGONS				CARNATIONS							

Fig. 4—21. A reproduction of the retail grower's crop rotation sheet. A portion of the retail growers greenhouse must be used as a sales area. This rotation sheet gives the utilization of greenhouse space throughout the year.

quantity as possible throughout the year. Foliage plants would be available continuously. In pot plants mums would be grown for Easter and Mother's Day, poinsettias for Christmas, and lilies for Easter. Geraniums and bedding plants would be produced for spring sales.

Greenhouse area: This retail greenhouse area would consist of four greenhouses, each 22 feet × 60 feet, plus flower shop, design area, and greenhouse work area. The houses would be connected in ridge and furrow arrangement. The first and third houses would be cross-benched with 10 benches, 4 feet × 18 feet. The second and fourth houses would be four benches, each 4 feet × 50 feet. A drop partition of poly film would be used between houses 3 and 4 during

Cut Mum Rotation — Pinched — For House 3   Apr 1972

Bench	Plant	Flower	Plant	Flower	Plant	Flower	Plant	Flower
3-1	Aug 28	Jan 1	Jan 8	Apr 23	Apr 30	Jul 30	Aug 6	Nov 19
3-2	Sep 11	15	22	May 7	May 14	Aug 13	20	Dec 3
3-3	25	29	Feb 5	14	21	20	27	24
3-4	Oct 9	Feb 12	19	21	28	27	Sep 3	Jan 7
3-5	23	26	Mar 5	Jun 4	Jun 11	Sep 10	17	21
3-6	Nov 6	Mar 5	12	11	18	24	Oct 1	Feb 4
3-7	20	19	26	25	Jul 2	Oct 8	15	18
3-8	Dec 11	26	Apr 2	Jul 2	9	15	22	25
3-9	25	Apr 9	16	16	23	29	Nov 5	Mar 4
3-10	Jan 1	16	23	23	30	Nov 5	12	11

Cutting Requirements —
    150   Spray
    100   Standard
    250   Total per Bench

Varieties —
    Mefos and Divinitys   Dec-Mar
    Indianapolis and Marbles   Apr
    Nob Hills and Icebergs   May
    Southerns and Marbles   Jun-Sep
    Indianapolis and Marbles   Oct-Nov

Fig. 4—22. A reproduction of the retail grower's cut mum rotation for house 3. This rotation was made by referring to the timing classification for cut mums, Fig. 4—4 and 4—5, and the mum cut flower scheduling table, Fig. 4—6. Because the classification is for single-stem crops, the first number was increased by two, which allows for two weeks of growth before pinching.

Cut MUM SCHEDULE BENCH 3-1
PLANT 8-28-72 PINCH 9-11
LIGHT 8-28 to 10-16 FLOWER 1-1-73

NUMBER	VARIETY
50	CENTENNIAL MEFO
50	GOLDBURST MEFO
50	DIVINITY
50	YEL. DIVINITY
50	DEMURE
250	

Fig. 4—23. A reproduction of the retail growers schedule sheet for one planting in a year-round cut mum program. The plant date, shade date, and flower date were obtained from the cut mum scheduling table (Fig. 4—6). A schedule sheet is made for each planting.

the heating season, so that house 4 could be operated at 50° F. night temperatures, while the rest of the range is at 60° F. (Fig. 4-21).

House 1 would be used generally for display and selling purposes. Two of the benches would be for foliage plants the year-round. The rest of the benches in this house would be used for pot plants for holidays, bedding plants in late spring, and garden supplies from spring to fall.

One of the benches in house 2 would be used for propagation and potting, and the other three benches would be in a rotation for natural-season mums, poinsettias, lilies, pot mums, geraniums, and bedding plants. After the natural-season mums were cut in the fall, the soil would be covered with black poly film, plus snow fence, in order to have a suitable base for setting pot plants. The poinsettias would be grown from 2¼-inch plants shipped in and panned in October.

A year-round cut chrysanthemum rotation would be used in house 3 (Fig. 4-22). This would be a pinched program, and each bench would hold 250 plants—50 each of three spray varieties and 50 each of two standard varieties. A bench of cut chrysanthemums would be harvested approximately every two weeks from this house.

House 4 would be used for a carnation and snapdragon rotation. One bench of carnations would be planted in mid-May and another in early June, and they would be in flower production until September and October of the following year when they would be followed by snapdragons. Such a rotation in this house would provide carnation flowers throughout the year and snapdragon flower production from January into May.

Reference Reviews

1. Ecke, Paul, Jr., and O. A. Matkin, *The Poinsettia Manual,* Paul Ecke Poinsettias, Encinitas, California, 1971. *An excellent source of information about any phase of poinsettia production, including cropping recommendations.*
2. Holley, W. D., and Ralph Baker, *Carnation Production,* William C. Brown Company, Inc., Dubuque, Iowa, 1963. *Chapter 6, "Control of Flowering Time," gives a complete presentation of the various factors affecting timing of carnation flowering. Recommendations are made for control of time of flowering.*

3. Langhans, Robert W., et al., *Chrysanthemums—A Manual of the Culture, Diseases, Insects, and Economics of Chrysanthemums*, New York State Extension Service and New York State Flower Growers Association, Inc., Ithaca, 1964. *Chapter 13, "Timing and Quality Control," contains a brief and general discussion on chrysanthemum timing.*

4. ————————————, *Snapdragons—A Manual of the Culture, Insects and Diseases, and Economics of Snapdragons*, New York State Extension Service and New York State Flower Growers Association, Inc., Ithaca, 1962. *Cropping of snapdragons is covered in Chapter 8, "Timing."*

5. Langhans, Robert W., D. C. Kiplinger, et al., *Easter Lilies—The Culture, Diseases, Insects, and Economics of Easter Lilies*, New York State Extension Service, Ithaca, and Cooperative Extension Service, Ohio State University, Columbus, 1967. *A detailed discussion of the various factors affecting Easter lily timing is presented in Chapter 10, "Timing."*

6. Laurie, Alex, D. C. Kiplinger, and Kennard S. Nelson, *Commercial Flower Forcing*, Seventh Edition, McGraw-Hill Book Company, New York, 1969. *Control of cropping is given for all major greenhouse flower and plant crops, and a detailed pot plant rotation is presented in Chapter 11, "Flowering Pot Plants."*

7. Mastalerz, John W., et al., *Geraniums—A Manual on the Culture, Diseases, Insects, Economics, Taxonomy, and Breeding of Geraniums*, Pennsylvania Flower Growers, University Park, 1971. *Chapter 14, "Scheduling," outlines various methods for handling geranium pot plant production and presents timetables and schedules.*

8. Mastalerz, John W., Robert W. Langhans, et al., *Roses—A Manual on the Culture, Management, Diseases, Insects, Economics, and Breeding of Greenhouse Roses*, Pennsylvania Flower Growers, University Park, New York State Flower Growers Association, Inc., Ithaca, and Roses, Inc., Haslett, Michigan, 1969. *A brief discussion of rose flower production timing is included in Chapter 11, "Timing, Pruning and Supporting."*

9. Miller, Robert O., and D. C. Kiplinger, *Poinsettias*, Extension Bulletin S. B. 15, Ohio State University, Columbus, 1963. *Control of cropping of poinsettias is presented in Chapter 9, "Control of Flowering by Daylength and Temperature."*

10. Nelson, Kennard S., *Flower and Plant Production in the Greenhouse*, The Interstate Printers & Publishers, Inc., Danville, Illinois, 1967. *Rotations and scheduling are given for the major flower and plant greenhouse crops, and a detailed rotation for pot plants is presented in Chapter 7, "Pot Plant Crops."*

CHAPTER 5

Management of the Greenhouse
Soil Environment

CHAPTER 5

The purpose of greenhouses is to provide the means for controlling the environment around plants. The glasshouses allow light energy to reach the plants; and moisture, air movement, and temperature may be adjusted as desired. The greenhouse structure and the equipment within it, plus the people involved, make it possible to provide the optimum conditions for plant growth and development the year-round.

The various parts of the environment are interrelated, and they cannot be considered singly without regard for the effect on the other parts of the environment as well as the total effect on the plants. Some of these relationships are obscure, others are clear, but all are easily overlooked. The discussion here is purposely divided into soil environment and air environment because our controls or adjustments are directly involved with one segment or the other.

The roots are the portion of the plant that happens to be most intimately associated with the soil environment and directly affected by changes there, and the stems' contact with the environment is primarily the air. Both portions of the greenhouse environment affect all parts of the plant, but for good management of the environment there must be an understanding of what the plant needs from the environment, what portions of the plant can receive these environmental qualities, and the means by which these qualities get to those portions of the plant.

In the soil the concern is to provide the best environment for the plant roots. There are some types of stems found in soils, but their requirements from the soil environment are much the same as those of the roots. The moisture and mineral nutrient requirements of the plants are met mainly by these two components of the environment passing into the roots of the plant. Thus the environment around the roots must have an adequate supply of moisture and the necessary minerals for the plant. In addition, because of the manner in which roots function, the environment must be suitable for the continuous growth of the roots. For this proper root development, the air supply around the roots must contain approximately the same quantity of oxygen as is found commonly in the air environment—about 20 per cent. Root growth and functioning proceeds best at temperatures from 50°F. to 70°F.

In the greenhouse there is not a general problem with management of temperature in the soil environment. The soil temperature adjusts closely to the air temperature, and the air temperature must be maintained someplace within these limits because of the temperature requirements for good plant growth. There are some situations that require special attention to soil temperatures. Several bulb crops are started at cool temperatures—outdoors in the fall, or in common or refrigerated storages—to provide vernalization and promotion of flowering. Root growth from the bulb is the first essential, and this requires temperatures around 50° F. or warmer. After the roots are well developed, the temperature may be lowered. In propagation of plants, root growth is promoted by higher temperatures—about 70°—, and means should be used to supply this temperature in the area of the roots or where rooting will take place.

Air will be available to the roots in the gaseous form—such as in the non-capillary pores of the soil—or will be dissolved in water, as it might be in the soil solution. In typical greenhouse operation sufficient air is or is not available in the soil environment, depending on the type of soil that is used, the bed, bench, or pot drainage capabilities, or the irrigation practices used. Air will diffuse to the area around the roots if it is physically possible to do so. The greenhouse operator does not have to pump air to the soil environment—all he has to do is provide the proper physical facilities so that the air under natural conditions can permeate the soil environment. Greenhouse soils must be coarse and porous (well supplied with non-capillary pores), benches and containers must drain readily and completely, and irrigations must be spaced sufficiently so that the soils dry somewhat between applications of water. These are the conditions that provide adequate air in the soil environment—set this stage and the air comes in automatically. This may sound rather simple, but failing to do this really is the most common pitfall in crop production management.

Plants need a continuous supply of water, and the main means of water entry into the plants is by the roots. The problem then is to maintain an adequate supply of moisture in the root environment. It would seem that this objective might be reached by keeping the soil environment constantly water-saturated, by using a soil which has a high retentive capacity for water, or by frequency of irrigation. The first proposal may be satisfactory for water lilies or rice, but for the vast majority of either greenhouse or field crops it would be entirely unsatisfactory because the lack of air in the water-saturated environment would limit root growth to such a extent that there may be no plant growth. Soils with high retentive capacities for water may be very desirable for use with field crops. The water supply for most field crops is dependent on rainfall, and in many areas the frequency of rainfall is not sufficient to supply the needs of the plants unless the soil retains the moisture. The water supply situation in the greenhouse is quite different from that with field crops. Within limits the greenhouse operator is able to supply water whenever it is needed.

In fact in recent years, because of improved irrigation systems and controls, the difficulty of employing qualified individuals to handle manual irrigation, and the use of mineral nutrient solutions for irrigation, the trend in the greenhouse has been toward the use of coarse and porous soils and frequent irrigation. Standard practice in the greenhouse is to supply water to the soil environment whenever it is needed, and when the application will not limit the air supply in the soil.

Mineral nutrients are required by plants, and they enter the plant through the roots in much the same fashion as water. For optimum plant growth the necessary minerals must be available in the environment about the roots, because the minerals usually enter the roots from the soil solution. A continuous supply of mineral nutrients in the soil environment would require either continuous additions of the minerals or the development of the minerals from products present within that environment. Management of mineral nutrition for greenhouse flower and plant crops requires careful planning and close supervision. The method most widely accepted is to irrigate each time with a nutrient solution that contains the necessary minerals.

• SOIL—THE ENVIRONMENT FOR PLANT ROOTS

It might be almost sacrilegious to suggest this, but there could be some advantages in referring to that substance in which roots are growing as *soil*. There are some hard fits with this term usage—such as hydroculture—, but this would not be much more difficult than trying to put a name on other materials which are used for root environments. It is assumed that this usage of the term *soil* may be acceptable—and it is used here respectfully but broadly.

Greenhouse operators through the years have taken many liberties with Mother Earth, and it is probable that they will take even more in the future. Of course these are attempts to improve the environment for the roots. It is intensive farming in the greenhouse, and it is possible to make modifications and adjustments to the soil that would not be practical or economical for field crops outdoors. It would be appropriate to acknowledge that the greenhouse operator uses tailor-made or manufactured soils as contrasted to the naturally derived soils used for agronomic crops. To cite an extreme example, in research as well as in commercial operation, greenhouse crops have been grown successfully in gravel—or possibly we should say the soil in which these crops were grown consisted of gravel—plus water, air, and nutrient minerals.

Regardless of terminology, location, or crops, plant roots must receive water, air, and nutrient minerals from their immediate environment.

• SOILS HAVE THREE PHASES—SOLID, LIQUID, AND GASEOUS

The solid phase is largely mineral, although most soils have some organic matter in them and a few are predominately organic. Soil solids have both chemical and physical effects on the soil environment. Depending on the kind of material of which it consists, the solid phase contributes minerals some of which may be essential nutrients for plants. These minerals enter the plant and may become chemically combined within it. Examples are calcium becoming available from limestone, and nitrates from organic matter. The physical effects may involve the attractive characteristics of the solid itself for mineral nutrients or water. This affects the supply and availability of these materials in the soil environment. If the solid phase is gravel or sand, mineral nutrients and water are held weakly and in small quantities, but clays attract them strongly and have a considerable adsorptive capacity. The size of the individual solid particles and the arrangement of these particles determines the size and amount of spaces among the solids.

Soils whose solid phase is gravel or sand have relatively few but large spaces among these rather large, solid particles. Clay on the other hand, because of the small size particles, packs closely together with very little space between the solid particles but with a great number of spaces. Granulated soils have large pores between the granules and small pores within each granule. To visualize the effect of particle size on the number and size of spaces among the particles it might help to mentally pack one 55-gallon drum with bowling balls and another drum with pinheads. Another physical contribution of the solid phase of the soil is that it provides anchor and support for the plants.

The liquid phase is water and the gaseous phase is air. The air and water of the soil are located in the spaces, commonly called pores, among the solid particles. The pores are rated by diameter as small, medium, and large—or maybe better yet, as capillary or non-capillary. The supply of water and air in the soil is dependent on the irrigation practices that are used in the greenhouse, the kind of solid material in the soil, and the quantity and diameter of the pores in the soil. In irrigation, water is usually applied to the surface of the soil, and it then percolates downward through the soil pores. The movement of the water may be slow, because a film of water first adheres to the soil solids and then the excess water starts the downward movement through the soil pores as the force of gravity exceeds the cohesive force of the water molecules for the water film on the soil solids. The water drains readily through the larger pores if there is unimpeded drainage through the bottom of the pot or bench. The small, capillary pores retain the water that is in them, because the force of adhesion for the pore walls is greater than the force of gravity. The extent of water drainage from a pore depends on the diameter of the pore, the amount of adhesion between pore wall and water, and the depth of the soil (Fig. 5-1).

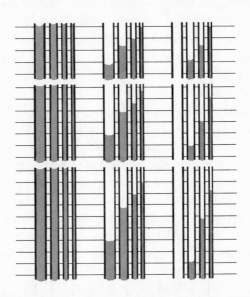

Fig. 5—1. Water drainage is affected by diameter and length of tube (pore). In each series of three sets of tubes, the first set was just filled with water, the second set indicates the water level after 5 minutes, and the last set shows the water level after 30 minutes. Water drains more readily from tubes if they are of larger diameter and of longer length. The diameter and length of soil pores affect water drainage from soil in that same way.

The smaller the diameter of the pore, the greater the adhesive force; and the deeper the soil, the greater the hydraulic head. As the water drains from the pores, air enters into them. There is an inverse relationship between soil air and water—as water content increases, air content decreases.

Field soils which are considered in condition for good plant growth are about one-half solid matter, one-fourth water, and one-fourth air by volume. However, it must be acknowledged that good field soil will have a different air-water relationship when the field soil is placed in benches or pots in the greenhouse. Water is applied to the soil frequently in the greenhouse, but may not drain from the soil so readily because of the shallow depths used in benches and pots. Because of this the good field soil placed in use in the greenhouse may actually consist of the same one-half solid matter, but of more water than under field conditions and less air. In fact frequently the air supply is so low that root growth is limited. Field soils must be amended to provide enough large pores so that under greenhouse conditions the water will drain through the soil readily and allow prompt infiltration of air (Fig. 5-2).

The study of soil science is a fascinating subject and there is a wealth of information available on field or naturally derived soils. In field conditions there is much more interest in the effects of the solid phase of soils on water and mineral nutrient retention, than there is in the greenhouse. For soils in greenhouse benches or pots, the first concern is for the adequacy of air in the soil—water and mineral nutrients will be added as required. Research has been conducted on greenhouse soils in several parts of the country, resulting in some specific recommendations for certain crops, but none of this work has developed basic literature in greenhouse soil science.

The result is that in greenhouse flower production, soils are referred to in general descriptive terms which are so broad and difficult to define that the same term may actually refer to different soil types. In the past, siltloam soils have been recommended for use in the greenhouse, and more recently coarse and porous soils. These terms seem to have a good and acceptable sound, and in some instances they might describe the soil accurately. There would be advantages, however, in using terms with more definite values. The greenhouse manager is most interested in the drainage characteristics of the soil under greenhouse conditions. There is no way to determine this by a visual inspection of the soil before use, and physical analysis of the soil in the past has been based on field conditions. In the field, the greater hydraulic head resulting from the greater depth of soil causes water to drain to a greater distance from the surface. It has been realized that the shallow depths used in the greenhouse affect drainage of water from the soil, but procedures for determining water drainage capabili-

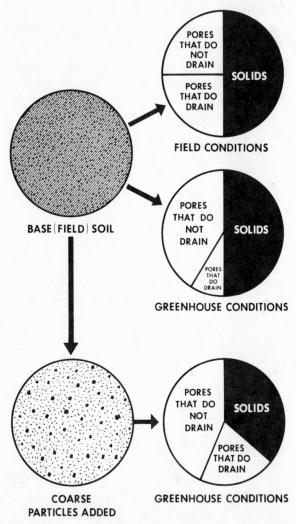

Fig. 5—2. Well drained field soil may not drain under greenhouse conditions. Good field soils have about 50 per cent solids and 50 per cent pores by volume, and under field conditions that volume of pores is about equally divided between those that drain and those that do not drain (about 25 per cent of the total volume of the soil drains). That same field soil brought into the greenhouse and placed in the typical shallow containers will still have the same relationship of pores to solids, but probably only about one-sixth of the pore volume drains (about 8 per cent of the total volume of the soil drains). If coarse organic matter is added to the field soil, the relationship may change to about 40 per cent solids and 60 per cent pores by volume, with about 30 per cent of that pore space draining under greenhouse conditions (about 20 per cent of the total volume of this soil drains).

ties of soil in greenhouse conditions had not been established. In order to have a good point of reference for greenhouse soils in this book, a soil-testing procedure was developed (Fig. 5-3).

On the basis of this analysis the field soils contained about 50 per cent solids and 50 per cent pores, but only about 20 per cent of these pores drained under greenhouse conditions; that would mean that in the entire soil mass 50 per cent would be solids, 40 per cent water, and 10 per cent air. When this field soil was amended so it was considered suitable for use with pot plants, it was about 35 per cent solids and 65 per cent pores, and about 25 per cent of these pores drained under greenhouse conditions; but that would mean that in the entire mass of the pot plant soil, 35 per cent was solids, 49 per cent water, and 16 per cent air. The same testing procedure was used on gravel, and the results were 47 per cent solids and 53 per cent pores, but 92 per cent of these pores drained. On the basis of this entire soil mass 47 per cent was solids, 4 per cent water, and 49 per cent air.

The purpose in developing the drainage test for soil was to provide a procedure which could be used commercially to determine if the drainage characteristics of the new soil mix were similar to those of the old mix that had been used satisfactorily. This should be a good tool in evaluating a soil mixture before it is put in use. The values given here are an indication of what may be expected, but they do not necessarily represent conditions that may exist for all greenhouse soils. By testing and then observing plant growth, each grower will be able to establish the reference values that are of significance for his local conditions.

● **THE BEST GREENHOUSE SOIL PROVIDES GOOD AERATION AT ALL TIMES**

The most certain way to assure good aeration in a greenhouse soil is to use gravel culture. Obviously there must be other limiting conditions with gravel culture or it would be used more universally. The primary points of consideration with gravel culture are that it must be irrigated more frequently, and the mineral nutrition program must be developed very carefully. In the greenhouse, frequent irrigations may not be of concern, other than the cost of the additional water

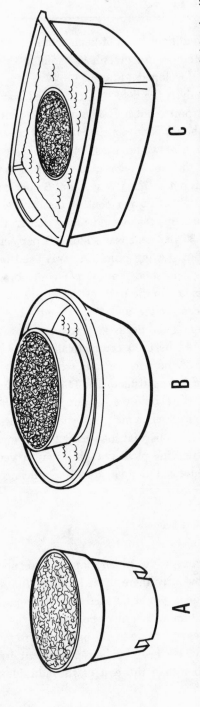

Fig. 5—3. Water drainage test for greenhouse soils. By means of this test, each grower can analyze his soils before planting and determine if the water drainage meets the standards of other soils he has used successfully. First make the test on a soil (either potting or bench soil) which drains well and is favorable for plant growth. Then make the test on the new soil mix before planting, compare results, and make the necessary adjustments to the soil mixture.

(A) Fill a plastic, 6-inch azalea pot with the soil mixture. Do not pack the soil in the pot, but from about a 3-inch height tap the pot on the counter top three times to settle the soil in the pot. The soil should be level with the top of the pot. (B) Subirrigate the pot of soil by placing it in a bowl with water about 3 inches above the pot bottom. Do not disturb for 24 hours. (C) Transfer the pot of soil to a deeper pan and bring the water level in the pan to the top edge of the pot. Keep the pot in this pan until water is visible at the soil surface. (Continued)

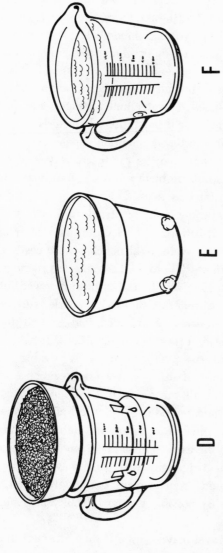

D   E   F

Fig. 5—3 (Cont'd). (D) Transfer the pot of saturated soil to the measuring glass (a one-quart measuring glass should accommodate the plastic pot about as sketched). Let the pot drain for four hours, record the amount of water that drained, and mark the level of the soil in the pot after draining. Discard the soil and wash the pot. (E) Plug the pot holes with florist clay and fill the pot with water to the soil level after draining. Measure and record the volume of water in the pot. The pot probably will contain more water than the one-quart measure will hold, but fill the measure to the quart level, dump, and measure the balance of the water in the pot. (F) Measure and fill the measure to the quart level of water in the pot.

To find the percentage of the pore volume that drained, as compared to the total volume of the soil, divide the amount of water that drained out of the pot by the total amount of water measured in the pot.

wasted, but for potted plants there usually would be a problem of supplying water often enough in the flower shop and in the home. It probably would be difficult to supply the mineral nutrients as needed in the shop and home, also. For these reasons, it does not seem reasonable that pot plants will be grown commercially in gravel culture. It would be appropriate to acknowledge at this time that pot plants grown in peat moss, such as azaleas commonly are, or pot plants produced in sand and peat mixtures are difficult to maintain in shop and home for the same basic reasons—lack of water and fertilizer. For pot plants then, the soil should approach the aeration characteristics of gravel, but with better water and fertilizer retention capacities.

Bench-grown cut flowers may be produced very well in gravel culture. There is no aeration problem with gravel culture and water and fertilizer may be added as needed. Earlier gravel culture procedures pumped the nutrient solution from tanks to water-tight benches and then allowed it to drain back to the tank for reuse. This system worked well, but the water-tight benches were costly to maintain, and it was nearly impossible to eradicate disease pathogens from tank and plumbing. More recently there has been renewed interest in the use of gravel culture, but this time with nozzle, surface irrigation on benches with free drainage provided. This system does waste some water and fertilizer, but there are no additional bench costs, and thorough steaming for disease pathogen control is possible.

The desirable features of using gravel for greenhouse soils are: (1) adequate aeration at all times with little if any change in extended use; (2) known and reproducible physical and chemical properties; and (3) easily automated irrigation and nutrition. Some of the potential problems with the use of gravel for greenhouse soils are: (1) the necessity of frequent irrigations, with some wasting of water and nutrients; (2) the exacting requirements for supplying all required mineral nutrients; and (3) possibly greater difficulty in planting than with conventional soils.

Various kinds of gravel may be used if they are inert and do not disintegrate. In the original procedures established at the Ohio Agricultural Experiment Station, B-grade haydite was used. The more recent work at Colorado State University used volcanic scoria or idealite. Because of shipping costs, local gravel will need to be used, and in most areas aggregates of similar physical and chemical properties can be obtained. The B-grade haydite used in Ohio was sized for ⅜-inch particles and finer. The Colorado researchers recommended scoria including all fractions passing ⅜-inch screen and idealite ranging from ⅛ inch to ⁵⁄₁₆ inch in size.

Gravel culture is not for everyone. It has some very good features, and when properly used can be an excellent method for producing flowers and plants in the greenhouse. But gravel culture is not a panacea. More conventional soils will continue to be used, but those who use them will have a better understanding of how to use them if they make a thorough investigation of gravel culture. Naturally derived soils to most growers continue to have an air of mysticism about them —they contribute some unknown quantities to plants. A knowledge of gravel culture helps dissolve these mystic qualities and brings the management of soil down to the basic requisites of air, water, and mineral nutrients.

THE GREENHOUSE OPERATOR MUST MAKE ADJUSTMENTS TO NATURALLY DERIVED SOILS

For crops that are going to be grown in the ground in the greenhouse, it might seem that if the soil had been suitable for field crops in that area it should be all right for flower crops, too. However, crops grown during the summer outdoors in natural conditions require a much different soil than crops being grown the year-round under glass in controlled conditions. It is necessary to apply water and mineral nutrients frequently to greenhouse crops for best growth, and it is important that the water drain away readily, leaving some of the soil pores free of water and containing air. Greenhouse ground needs to be tile drained so that it is certain that water will flow away from the lower levels of the soil, and adjustments must be made to the soil above the tile level so that there is a great enough portion of soil pores large enough to drain sufficiently in order to allow an adequate air supply in the soil. Because of the continual cropping of the greenhouse soil, it is necessary to make adjustments to the soil between crops to maintain good drainage and aeration.

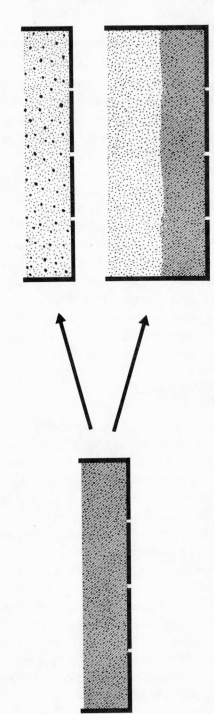

Fig. 5—4. Water drainage in greenhouse soils can be improved by adding coarse particles to the soil mixture or by increasing the depth of the soil. In most instances it is more practical to incorporate some organic matter into the soil than it is to increase the depth. It should be noted that when the depth is increased the improved water drainage is in the upper levels of the soil.

The tile for greeenhouse ground beds should be about 15 inches deep and 18 inches apart on centers. Three-inch tile is usually used, and a fall of one to 2 inches per 100 feet is required. Of course to be effective, the low end of the tile line must drain freely into an open ditch or a larger tile line which drains freely. If the arrangements are made at the time the tile drainage is installed, the system may be used also for steaming the soil between crops.

Ground beds have about one foot of soil above the tile lines. That is a shallow soil on a field soil basis, but a deep soil as compared to soil used for greenhouse pots and benches (Fig. 5-4). A soil pore of the same diameter may drain several inches down from the soil surface in the field soil with an effective 30-inch pore length, may drain only an inch in the greenhouse ground bed with the one-foot soil depth, and may not drain of water at all with the 6-inch pore length in the greenhouse bench or pot. For the same degree of soil aeration, the soil in the greenhouse ground bed must have larger pores than the field soil, and the bench and pot soil must have larger pores than the ground bed soil.

The adjustment which is made to field soil in preparation for use in the greenhouse must produce soil pores sufficiently large so that they drain in greenhouse conditions—shallow soil depths and frequent irrigations. The addition of organic matter to soils promotes the aggregation of the individual soil particles into groups (granules), and this produces the larger soil pores required for good soil drainage (Fig. 5-4). Different types of organic matter may be used, but chopped straw is the best for bench soils. The amount of organic matter that should be used depends on the porosity status of the soil. In common terminology, the addition of organic material makes the soil lighter weight. The general concept is that clay soils are heavy and sandy soils and loam are light. This may not be bad terminology if we appreciate that the weight difference represents the increased amount of water held in the "heavy" soil.

Although the soils that we work with have various degrees of wetness, we never have soils that are completely devoid of water. The solid phase of clay soils may actually weigh less than the solid phase of loam or sandy soils, and the clay soils may have more total pore space. The pore spaces in the clay soils, however, are of such small diameter that they retain water in spite of the gravitational attraction.

- ### STEAMING IS THE BEST METHOD FOR ERADICATING PESTS, DISEASE PATHOGENS, AND WEEDS FROM GREENHOUSE SOILS

The controlled environment of the greenhouse is conducive to growth of pests, disease pathogens, and weeds, as well as the crop plants. Every means should be used to eliminate the source of these problems before they get started, and the most efficient and economical soil treatment is heat. If the soil is heated to 180°F. and held there for a minimum of 30 minutes, the pests, disease organisms, and weeds will be eliminated. Soil thermometers should be placed in the soil at the point expected to heat the slowest. Different methods for heating soil may be used, but steaming is by far the best. Although the top temperature required for the heat treatment is 180°F., because of the characteristics of steam the temperature does proceed to 212°F. or thereabouts. To raise the temperature of one cubic foot of greenhouse soil from 60°F. to 212°F. in one hour would require about 3,500 BTU. That quantity of heat could be obtained from 3.6 pounds of steam because 970 BTU are required to change one pound of water at 212°F. to one pound of steam at the same temperature. Conversely, when steam condenses to water, each pound of steam gives off 970 BTU of heat to the surroundings. Because about 50 per cent of the heat developed at the boiler will be lost in transmission through the mains and to the air during the steaming process, it is necessary to develop about 7 pounds of steam at the boiler for each cubic foot of soil to be steamed per hour.

Boiler capacities are rated variously; however, pounds of steam per hour seems to be accepted in most areas, and it does give an accurate rating of the boiler capability. If the boiler rating is in terms of 1,000 BTU output per hour (MBH), it may be converted to pounds steam per hour by dividing the value by .970.

A greenhouse bench 3½ feet × 100 feet, with 6-inch soil depth, contains 175 cubic feet of soil. The minimum boiler capacity would be 1,225 pounds of steam per hour for steaming 175 cubic feet of soil. A ground bed of the same dimensions theoretically would require twice as much steam because the soil is twice the depth, but practically it would require considerably more. With ground beds it is not possible to steam just the area in which the plants will be placed or a single bed at a time. An entire section must be steamed, including the walks between the beds. The ground bed 3½ feet × 100 feet with one foot of soil above the tile, because of the adjacent areas which would have to be steamed also, would contain about 540 cubic feet of soil and would require a minimum boiler capacity of 3,780 pounds of steam per hour.

Potting soil or soil in flats usually is steamed in chests or carts equipped for that purpose. The required steam capacity at the boiler would be computed in the same manner—multiply the number of cubic feet of soil to be treated by 7.

When the steam is exhausted into the soil it is approximately at atmospheric pressure, regardless of the steam pressure in the boiler or in the lines. The only advantage in using high pressure steam for steaming soil is that a greater quantity of steam can be transported to the area to be treated per size pipe.

Before steaming, the soil should be completely prepared for planting so that as soon as it cools after steaming, the plants can be set. This preparatory work will include tilling or spading, incorporating organic matter, possibly adding some mineral nutrients, and making sure that the moisture content of the soil is about right for planting. The soil should be handled as little as possible after steaming to avoid contamination. It is important that the moisture content is about right for planting, as heat penetration will be slow through dry soil, and soil that is too wet requires much more heat to bring it to 180° to 212°F. than moderately moist soil.

The steam must be distributed throughout the soil in ground beds by means of buried conductors. The most sensible arrangement is to use drainage tile about 15 inches deep and on 18-inch centers.

For soil in benches, the steam may be distributed by either buried or surface conductors. The use of surface conductors saves time and labor, and the results can be perfectly satisfactory. One conductor will suffice for benches to 3-foot width. Wider benches require two conductors the length of the area to be steamed. Porous canvas hose may be used for a surface conductor. The distribution of steam through it is good, and it is more convenient to use than pipe or tile.

For a steam distribution system in chest or cart for steaming potting soil, one-inch pipe should be spaced on 9-inch centers, with ⅛-inch holes drilled every 9 inches on the bottom side of the pipe. There are various possibilities in design of this steaming equipment, depending on the situation. There are definite advantages in steaming the potting soil right on the bench or cart where it will be used.

If steam is to effectively permeate the soil mass, it must replace the soil air. If steam is to replace the soil air, the air must have a free means of escape from the soil. For soil in benches, the means of escape is through the drainage holes at the bottom of the bench. This is just another reason for making certain that the bench drainage is good in preparing the soil. For chest and cart steaming, they must not be closed or covered tightly until the air has had a chance to escape. The only means for the air to get away from the soil in ground beds is from the surface. For this reason, when ground beds are steamed the cover should not be placed over the soil until after the steam has been introduced for awhile.

The soil must be covered during steaming so that the steam will be contained and the soil will be brought up to temperature. Lightweight vinyl covers are suitable for this purpose. As soon as the soil has reached 180°F. for 30 minutes, the cover should be removed in order to allow excess moisture to evaporate and to prevent excessive steaming of the soil.

• SOIL MAY BE TREATED CHEMICALLY IF STEAM IS NOT AVAILABLE

Some chemicals may be used to eradicate soil pests, disease organisms, and weeds. The disadvantages of using chemicals rather than steam are: (1) They cannot be used in the vicinity of crop plants—this limits the use to treating an entire area or house at a time rather than a bench as needed: (2) the soil may not be planted for about two weeks after treatment; (3) the residues from some chemicals are toxic to some crop plants; (4) the cost per unit area treated is more than steaming; and (5) the minimum soil temperature is 50°F., with best results at about 70°F. Soils to be treated with chemicals must be prepared for plants in the same way as they are for steaming.

Methyl bromide is packed under pressure in cans—one pound liquid methyl bromide per can. When the pressure is released in the can by puncturing it, the liquid methyl bromide vaporizes and expels from the can. The soil to be treated is covered with a plastic film which is supported or suspended several inches above the soil, so that the methyl bromide vapor when it is injected under the film has free access to all portions of the soil surface. The methyl bromide applicator is a simple clamp device and punch, with plastic tubing attached. The end of the tubing is placed under the soil cover, and when the can is punctured the vapor flows through the tubing to the soil area to be treated. For good distribution of the gas, place the cans in water at about 150°F. for a few minutes before puncturing them.

The rate of treatment is 4 pounds of methyl bromide per 100 cubic feet of soil. For ground beds it may be assumed that the effective treatment will penetrate one foot below the surface, if the soil is prepared in good planting condition. The cover should be kept in place for 48 hours and then removed, and the soil aired for about two weeks before planting. Actually the length of time between treating and planting will vary with soil type, temperature, and irrigation.

Methyl bromide treatment should not be used for carnation soils.

Chloropicrin is more difficult to use than methyl bromide, but it is less costly. It may be injected into the soil by machine or hand applicators at the rate of 3 cc., 6 inches deep on 12-inch squares. The treated area may be covered with plastic film after the chloropicrin is injected, or the soil surface may be sealed with water by wetting the top inch of soil. The soil surface must be kept moist, or the area must be covered with plastic for 48 hours. The soil must be aired for two weeks before planting.

Vapam 4S is a water-soluble liquid which changes when applied to the soil and forms methyl isothiocyanate gas. One quart of Vapam is placed in 2 or 3 gallons of water in a sprinkling can, and this solution is sprinkled uniformly over 100 square feet of soil. After the application the soil should be irrigated to a depth of 6 inches. About one week after treatment the soil should be cultivated sufficiently to break the surface, and then planting can take place about one week later.

• THERE ARE FEW IF ANY HERBICIDES WHICH MAY BE USED SAFELY ON GREENHOUSE SOILS

Fortunately most greenhouse soils are steamed, and that provides excellent weed control in the crop soil. For weeds in walks or under benches, it may be possible to use one or two herbicides; but it must be established thoroughly that the material will not have a bad effect on the crop plants. Many greenhouse crops have been ruined because weed killers have been used in or around greenhouses. If you do not know which weed killer can be used safely, get the recommendation from the state extension specialist.

The greenhouse manager must be aware also that materials brought into the greenhouse may be sufficiently contaminated with herbicides to cause crop damage. One of the worries currently is the use of field soils that may have been treated for control of weeds in farm crops. The soil that is brought in not only must be the right type but must have a history of no herbicide treatments also. Lumber or pipe brought in from storage yards that were treated with weed killers has seriously damaged greenhouse crop plants, too.

Greenhouse crops such as hydrangeas, that are usually grown outdoors for a portion of the year, may have to be placed on soil outdoors that is not steamed. There is a temptation to use herbicides on such soils before setting the hydrangea pots down, but by far the better procedure is to cover the field with black polyethylene film and set the pots on top of it. The film should be punctured enough so that water will drain through it. It can provide almost perfect weed control.

• PLANTS MUST RECEIVE A SUFFICIENT QUANTITY OF WATER

In order for the plant to receive enough water the root system must be large enough for the size of the plant, the roots must be actively growing, and there must be an adequate supply of moisture in the soil. It is a good grower who fully appreciates the relationship between the roots and the rest of the plant. Something of a sixth sense is required to keep abreast of root conditions—or maybe it is not so much the ability to determine root growth as it is to continuously remember to make the evaluation.

There are times in normal operations when there will not be sufficient roots to supply the water requirements of the plant. When unrooted cuttings are stuck it becomes an interesting contest of conserving the water content within the plant by limiting transpiration while providing the optimum conditions for root development. One of the most effective means of limiting transpiration is to keep the leaves moist by intermittent misting. The mist must be controlled effectively, however, so that there is adequate air in the soil at all times. Misting from three to six seconds, from one to three minutes apart, gives moisture coverage on the leaves without undue run-off to the soil. As roots develop on the cutting, the control of transpiration should be correspondingly relaxed.

When rooted cuttings are planted they usually have the right quantity of roots for the size of the plant, but the roots are not in active growth at the time of planting. Here again is a root development-transpiration contest—but of shorter duration than with the unrooted cutting. Active root growth should be evident in rooted cuttings within three days after they are planted. The same timing for root growth could be expected for transplanted seedlings, but dormant plants may require a few more days.

Root growth in bulbs must precede shoot growth. Bulbs which are planted and then placed in cool temperatures to promote shoot growth should be held at a minimum of 48°F. until well rooted, and then the temperature may be reduced.

Unfortunately there are times when there is an unexpected or unscheduled loss of roots or cessation of root growth. When this occurs there are two courses of action—locate the cause and conserve the water within the plant until root growth is established again. The most effective means for conserving water within the plant is by limiting transpiration. The method for reducing transpiration will have to vary with the situation, but it could involve increasing the relative humidity of the air by misting and reducing light intensity and air movement. It is difficult to effectively reduce transpiration in large plants. There are many causes for root problems. The most common ones are: deficiency of oxygen in the soil, excess of fertilizer in soil, pests and diseases.

When there is a deficiency of oxygen in the soil, too many of the soil pores contain water rather than air. There are several reasons why there may be excess water in the soil—there may not be free drainage away from the soil because of ground, bench, or pot conditions. The only solution here is to provide the free drainage required. Drainage problems are always handled much more easily before the crop is planted. However, if the plants are in place some remedial action may be taken—tile in ground beds may be unplugged, holes may be drilled in the bottom of benches, and drainage holes in pots may be unplugged. If the drainage from the soil cannot be sufficiently improved while the crop is in place, it will help to space irrigations as far apart as possible, and with bench or bed crops it may be possible to irrigate the poorly drained areas less frequently than the well drained ones.

The soil itself may not drain of water. The solid phase of the soil may consist of very small particles which pack together tightly, forming very small diameter soil pores that retain water against the pull of gravity. Soil depth may be a factor in drainage of water through the soil. The downward pull on water in the pores is greater in long pores (deep soils) than in short ones (shallow soils). About the only corrective action that can be taken is to make proper adjustments in applying water. Irrigations should be spaced as far apart as possible, and the amount of water applied each time reduced.

Too frequent irrigations may be a cause of poor aeration in the soil and the resulting poor root growth. Except with very coarse and porous soils there always is the possibility that the air will be limited in the soil if water is applied too often.

There may be too much fertilizer in the soil for good root growth. This problem is very common with greenhouse crops and too frequently overlooked. The excess fertilizer problem may result from applying fertilizer too frequently, applying too much fertilizer at a time, or not applying a sufficient quantity of water each irrigation; it may also be due to poor soil drainage or poor drainage away from pot or bench. If there is any reason to suspect a root problem, the soil should be tested with a Solu Bridge immediately. This is an accurate evaluation of the fertilizer status of the soil and can be done rapidly and easily. It will promptly establish if the root problem may be related to fertilizer excess. It is not unusual, in fact it is quite common, that the problem is caused by a combination of irrigation and fertilizer application practices.

Pests may limit the effectiveness of roots. The most common root pests through the years have been symphilids and nematodes. More recently the fungus gnat larva has been recognized as a serious root problem in many greenhouse plants. The root pests may ingest the root tips, thus limiting the means of water entry into the plant; or they may enter the root, competing for plant fluids and plugging the water-conducting tubes in the plant. Symphilids and nematodes may be eliminated from the soil by steaming. Reinfestation by these two pests occur if plants infested with them are placed in the soil or if infested soil is introduced to the steamed soil. Symphilids are white—about ¼ inch long when fully grown—and they have 12 pair of legs, and antennae or feelers that are constantly in motion. They stay in the moist areas of the soil, and when fresh soil is exposed slowly by trowel or shovel the symphilids may be observed scurrying for cover. The antennae and the fast movement when exposed in the soil are the most easily recognized traits of symphilids.

Special training and equipment are required to locate and identify nematodes. It also is difficult to diagnose the problem from the appearance of the root. Root knot nematodes may produce characteristic "knotted" roots, but the effects of other nematodes may be hard to identify. Many of the state universities or experiment stations have personnel qualified to diagnose nematode problems. Because of the length of time roses are grown in the same soil and the method of propagation which is used, nematodes are more commonly a problem with roses than other greenhouse crops.

The fungus gnat larva is colorless to white, and at maturity it is only ¼ inch long. It is the larval stage in the life cycle of the fungus gnat. The entire cycle from egg to egg takes two to four weeks. The adult fungus gnat lives for only a week, but during that period the female has the potential of laying 1,000 eggs. The adult is black and tiny, but fungus gnats are easily observed because they often swarm about the face. The larva, the stage that is doing the damage by feeding on the roots and possibly the stem of the plant, is not so easily noticed. Control may be directed toward the larva or the adult or both.

Diseases may destroy the roots or plug the conducting tissues of roots or stems. The plant pathogens *Rhizoctonia solani* and *Pythium spp.* seem to be present universally in greenhouse soils; unless the soils are steamed or treated chemically to eliminate these fungi, many of the plants grown in the greenhouse become infected with them, and stem and/or root diseases result.

In addition to Rhizoctonia stem rot and Pythium root rot the most common diseases caused by soil-borne pathogens are: Phytophthora root rot in snapdragons, lilies, and bedding plants caused by *Phytophthora spp.*, Thielaviopsis root rot in poinsettias and snapdragons from *Thielaviopsis basicola*, Verticillium wilt in roses, chrysanthemums, and snapdragons caused by *Verticillium alboatrum*, Fusarium wilt in carnations from *Fusarium oxysporium f. dianthi*, bacterial wilt in carnations from *Pseudononas caryophylli*, and bacterial stem rot and leaf spot of geraniums caused by *Xanthomonas pelargoni*. The symptoms of these various diseases may appear similar because the damage to the roots or the impairment of conducting tissues in the stem prevents the movement of water and nutrients into the plant to much the same extent, regardless of the name of the disease or the pathogen causing it. If the soil is carefully steamed before planting, the plant pathogens will be eliminated, and it may be expected that the plants placed in the soil will remain disease-free until pathogens are introduced to the plants or to the soil. If the soil becomes infested after planting, it may be possible to control the rate of growth of the pathogens by regulation of temperature and moisture and the application of appropriate chemicals. It must be determined first which pathogen is involved, because the various pathogens may be controlled by different materials. The disease symptoms caused by different pathogens may look very similar. If there is any question about the cause of the disease, it is essential to get professional help in making the diagnosis. Most flower production greenhouses do not have the equipment nor the personnel to make positive identification of the cause for the various diseases that might occur, but the manager must know whom he can depend on for prompt diagnosis and recommendations for control.

• MOISTURE IS LOST FROM THE SOIL THROUGH DRAINAGE, EVAPORATION, AND PLANTS

It may be poor terminology to say that soil water is lost through the plant, but the plant's gain is actually the soil's loss in this instance. The larger the plants, the greater the water loss from the soil to the plants. Plants by weight are about 90 per cent water, but the total amount of water taken into a plant is much greater than that because of the loss of water from the plant by transpiration—the evaporation from the surface of leaves and stems. It has been calculated that the water loss per day by transpiration from some plants is equal to twice the weight of the plant. The rate of evaporation of water from the soil depends on soil type, amount of moisture in the soil, temperature, air movement, the relative humidity of the air, and the exposure of the soil surface to the sun. Water loss from the soil usually is much greater during the summer than during the winter.

Loss of water from the soil by means of drainage depends on soil type and structure, the freedom of water movement from bench, bed, or pot, and the depth of the soil. In a Colorado study with carnations, it was found that approximately 27 per cent of the applied water drained away, and 73 per cent of the water which was applied was available for use by the plant and for evaporation from the soil.

Because of the many variables, it is difficult to estimate the amount of water loss from soils. For cut flowers growing in benches or beds, the water loss from the soil may possibly vary from one quart per square foot per week to one gallon per square foot per week. For cut flowers growing in gravel, probably four times that quantity of water would be lost because of the frequency of application and the free drainage through the gravel. For pot plants in 6-inch pots, the water loss per pot per day possibly may vary from ¼ pint to one pint.

• ENOUGH WATER MUST BE APPLIED WITH EACH APPLICATION

Sufficient water must be applied so that some water drains through the bottom of the bench, beds, or containers. For normal irrigation this will be about ½ gallon of water per square foot of soil each irrigation, for cut flowers in bench or bed. For the first watering after planting there may be an advantage, particularly during the winter, in spot watering each plant rather than the entire soil mass. Sufficient water must be applied so that the soil is wetted for the entire depth under each plant and there is some run through, but so that there are dry areas between the rows of plants. Spot watering may require one quart or less per square foot of soil.

On occasion it is necessary to leach soil with water in order to reduce the amount of fertilizer or soluble salts in the soil. Leaching requires an application of one gallon or more water per square foot of soil. If heavy leaching is required, it may not be possible to put on a sufficient quantity of water in a single application. The succeeding applications should follow immediately, so that the soil remains saturated for the shortest possible time.

Plants in 6-inch pots should be given about ½ pint of water each irrigation.

It is essential to establish the quantity of water delivered from each method of irrigation that is used. If watering is done with hose-in-hand, it is simple to determine the amount of water delivered by observing the length of time it takes to fill a 5-gallon pail. For somewhat average greenhouse conditions and for watering cut flowers with the faucet opened fully and using a 50 foot, ¾-inch hose, the water delivery is around 12 gallons per minute; it would require 25 seconds to fill a 5 gallon pail. With hose-in-hand, it would require 15 minutes for one man to water a cut flower bench 3½ feet × 100 feet.

Reduced water flow must be used for watering pot plants—about 3 gallons per minute. With hose-in-hand about 1½ seconds would be required for watering each 6-inch pot.

To determine the water delivery from other methods of water distribution it may be necessary to use a water meter. In some instances it may be possible to make the reading with the main meter if the water system being tested is the only demand for water during the test period. If it is not possible to measure the flow in that way, a water meter usually may be borrowed from the water company and temporarily installed at the site to be tested.

- ## THE FREQUENCY OF IRRIGATION
  IS A MANAGEMENT DECISION

When to water is a critical decision because it determines the amount of air as well as the amount of water that is available to the plant. Too frequent applications of water may limit the air supply in the soil to such an extent that the roots may be damaged. This is commonly referred to as *overwatering*; unfortunately, to many individuals the term implies that too much water was applied per application.

Water must be applied often enough so that there is a sufficient amount for the plants at all times, but not so often that the air is limited in the soil. Tensiometers have been used with some degree of success to sense the moisture content of the soil, but they are generally considered inadequate for commercial use. Undoubtedly a device will be developed eventually which may be used for sensing moisture and/or air content of greenhouse soils, but until that time visual inspection of the soil by human beings continues to be the best means of determining when to irrigate. Inspection of the soil surface is not enough to make a decision on the soil's need for water. The observation must be made below the soil surface by digging into the soil in cut flower benches or knocking pot plants out of pots. The decision of when to irrigate must be made by an individual with experience—it is not the sort of thing that can be passed off to just anybody.

Some growers base their opinion of when to water on the first signs of wilting of the plants. Wilting does indicate a lack of moisture in the plants, but it does not necessarily mean that there is insufficient moisture in the soil. Because of pests or disease the root system may be so limited that not enough water can enter the plants. Adding more water to the soil in such a situation may aggravate the problem rather than relieve it. Plants may wilt when the sun first appears after a period of overcast, cool weather. This wilting does indicate that insufficient water is being taken into the plants, but it does not necessarily mean that there is a lack of water in the soil. When wilting occurs while there is enough water in the soil, the best action to take is to reduce the water loss from the plants by providing partial shade over them or by increasing the relative humidity of the air by misting. If the wilting of plants does in fact indicate a lack of moisture in the soil, the water deficiency in the soil should have been detected by other means earlier.

The individual who schedules irrigation must know the air/moisture potential of the soils involved. If the soil is gravel, it is almost impossible to water too frequently, but clay soils are easily irrigated too often.

Future weather conditions should be considered in scheduling irrigation. If dark and cool weather conditions are expected, irrigation may be delayed a day or two, but if it is thought that it will be sunny and warm, the irrigation should be scheduled. Much the same reasoning is used on a 24-hour basis. The primary demand for water in the plant is during the daylight hours, and this is one of the reasons irrigation is done during the morning in anticipation for that demand.

The frequency of irrigation must be based on the kind and size of plant. Some kinds of plants use more water than others, and some have roots which are sensitive to limited air supply in the soil. Plants with high water demand, such as hydrangea, develop leaf burn without adequate supplies of water. Pothos is an example of the plants that are killed easily by too frequent irrigation. The water requirements of small plants are less than those of large plants, and this must be taken into consideration in scheduling irrigation. The stage of growth of the plants has an effect on their water use. Plants in vigorous vegetative growth use more water than at the stage when flower buds are forming. The water demand again will be greater when the plant is in full flower. Irrigating less frequently at time of flower bud formation is sometimes referred to as *toning*.

• WATER DISTRIBUTION SYSTEMS MAY VARY FROM MAN WITH SPRINKLING CAN TO COMPLETELY AUTOMATED SYSTEMS

There may not be much water distribution to plants anymore by sprinkling can, but there was a day when it was considered that that highly personal arrangement between man and plant was essential. The attempt through the years has been to get the water to the individual plants as well or better with a reduced amount of man power. This has led to subirrigation and many different forms of surface irrigation.

It does not appear that subirrigation will be used commercially as a means of distributing water to plants, primarily because of the difficulty in providing and maintaining water-tight benches. Several distribution systems are satisfactory for surface irrigation.

The water distribution system must wet the entire soil mass evenly; it must not have harmful effects to the soil; the water should be distributed within a short period of time; and the installation and operating expense must be economical. A brief evaluation of some existing water distribution systems will illustrate these points. Distributing water with hose-in-hand may be one of the very best means of wetting the soil mass evenly if the operator is adequately trained, but it can possibly have some harmful effects on the soil. If water breakers are not used, the soil becomes compacted; and the soil may be splashed out of the pots. The installation costs for this system are very small, but the operating costs are very high. Worse than that, it is not possible to have enough trained help to distribute the water when it is needed. For these reasons the attempts have been to replace the manual labor with equipment. Tubes that distribute water to the soil by means of piddle or nozzles that spray the water over the soil surface can be effective means of taking care of a large area of soil in a minimum amount of time—they are fast. They may not do so good a job of wetting the entire soil mass as a good man with hose-in-hand; and the entire area in the system has to be treated the same, with all of the pots or the entire bench of cut flowers having to be watered at one time. These systems are certain to eliminate some of the good growers' finesse, but the change may be inescapable. Piddle and spray systems are used most successfully on coarse, porous soil, but there may be some problem with piddle systems and uneven water distribution, because the water moves directly downward with little lateral dispersion, if the soil is too porous.

The piddle or spray water distribution systems do not seem to cause any soil problems such as compaction.

The big advantage in the piddle or spray system is in the ease and economy of operation. If the system is controlled manually, the grower would be able to irrigate three to six times the amount of area than he would with hose-in-hand. If electrical controls are used with the system, considerably more area can be managed with the same man power.

Installation costs for water distribution systems may seem high, but when they are compared with the possible savings in labor, there just is no other direction to go. Equipment costs vary with the type of system installed and the economy of the country, but a system for a cut flower bench might be from 10 cents to 20 cents per lineal foot of bench. The water distribution equipment should give good service for three years or longer before it needs to be replaced, which would make the yearly cost per lineal foot of bench space from about 3 cents to 7 cents. For a 3½-foot bench, that would place the cost for water distributing equipment at about 1 cent per square foot of bench area per year—certainly a modest expenditure. It requires about 15 minutes for one man with hose-in-hand to water a bench 3½ feet × 100 feet. If he waters the bench twice a week, that would be about 100 irrigations during the year for the 350-square-foot area with a total man power expenditure of 1,500 minutes or about 4 minutes per square foot per year. If this man were paid $2.00 per hour, the labor cost for irrigation would be about 13 cents per square foot per year. If he had water distribution equipment and could handle three times more area than with hose-in-hand, there would be a saving in labor of about 8 cents per square foot per year, which would more than pay the yearly cost for irrigation equipment and the installation costs.

The values that are used in this illustration are approximations and averages. Each manager should make his own study of irrigation equipment and labor costs in order to determine the most favorable means of irrigation at his greenhouse.

The cost of equipment for water distribution on pot plants may vary considerably, but it may run about 10 cents per pot for the systems with small-diameter piddle tubes to each pot. If the equipment can be used for a minimum of three years before being replaced, that would bring the cost down to about 3 cents per year per pot location. If four crops of pots were produced in the area per year, the equipment cost would be less than 1 cent per pot produced. With hose-in-hand it requires about one and one-half seconds to water each pot; and for a 12-week crop watered once a day, that would require a total watering time of about two minutes per pot per crop. For labor at $2.00 per hour, that would be an irrigation labor cost of about 7 cents per pot per crop. If three times as many pots could be handled with the same labor cost, that would be a savings of about 4 cents per pot, which would cover the cost of irrigation equipment and installation.

It should be acknowledged here that, although it appears from this discussion that water distribution systems are more economical to operate than hose-in-hand methods of irrigation, it will be up to the manager to put the labor that is saved to other productive employment in the greenhouse.

- ### ELECTRIC CONTROLS WITH ELECTRIC WATER VALVES AND TIMERS SHOULD BE PUT IN

This is the next important step, if water distribution systems are installed. Using electric power to control irrigation not only releases some labor for other work in the greenhouse, but makes it possible to irrigate when the labor is not on duty, such as early morning, Sundays, and holidays. The first step in planning electric control of irrigation is to decide how many areas or units should be irrigated at one time. With cut flowers it usually is best to have individual controls for each bench, because the decision to irrigate must be made bench by bench. With pot plants the unit to be irrigated should be a production unit of plants of the same kind and at the same stage of growth. An electric water valve will then be required for each one of these areas or units. Usually diaphragm water valves are used for irrigation, and the same size valve can be used as the pipe size of the water distribution system for that area or unit.

The second decision to make is the number of units that can be irrigated at one time, and this is determined by the water capacity that is available in the greenhouse. If the available water volume is sufficient for irrigating any two units at the same time, two controllers could be used without need for coordinating them. If there is just enough water available to handle an area at a time, the controller should be large enough so that all areas to be irrigated can be programmed on the same controller; or if two or more controllers are used, they would have to be timed so that they operate at different time periods.

In most instances there are advantages in having the control unit as close as possible to the areas being serviced. This provides for the minimum length of wire needed from controller to water valves, and the controller is then positioned conveniently for the manager of that section to make the necessary selections. Some of the control systems are quite sophisticated and highly efficient, but they cannot think or reason. It still will be necessary to have a competent human being make the decision of which area should be watered and then make the necessary settings on the controller.

In choosing a controller it is necessary to know the minimum and maximum irrigation times that will be required for the crops in the area. Pot plants may be watered for about 5 minutes and cut flowers for about 10 minutes; but this varies considerably among greenhouses, depending on the water distribution equipment that is used, the soil situation, and the crop.

• THE MINERAL NUTRIENT STATUS OF THE SOIL MAY BE DETERMINED BY THREE MEANS

The status may be determined by the appearance and growth of the plants, by soil analysis, or by plant analysis. Regardless of how it is determined, the appearance and growth of the plants must be part of the analysis. It must be established first that root growth is good, because if it is not good the required nutrients will not get into the plant regardless of the status of the minerals in the soil. There are three common causes of poor root growth: (1) poor soil aeration; (2) too great a supply of soluble minerals in the soil; and (3) damage to the roots from pests or disease. It should be emphasized here that lack of mineral nutrients in the soil is not a common cause of poor root growth, and the addition of more minerals to the soil before good root growth is established may be harmful. The appearance of the upper portions of plants will indicate mineral deficiencies in the plant, even with the adequate supply of the mineral in the soil, if the roots are not in good growth.

It is not recommended that soil fertility be regulated solely on the

basis of the appearance of the plants, because it is difficult to make
consistently accurate diagnoses on the basis of these symptoms, and
in other instances plant growth may be impaired if soil fertility adjustment is not made until the symptom appears. It is only the most experienced growers who can detect and evaluate the symptoms of mineral
deficiency in plants.

Nitrogen deficiency in soils—and plants—is quite common, and it
probably produces some of the most easily recognized symptoms in
plants—small leaves, light green leaf color, and short growth. In spite
of these symptoms' being rather easily recognized, usually by the
time the symptom is noticed the deficiency of nitrogen in the plant
has adversely affected the quality and quantity of plant growth. It
is difficult to recognize nitrogen deficiency symptoms in the early stages
of plant growth, and this is very critical in determining the number of
stems that will develop, the length of stem, and the rate of growth.
Other mineral deficiency symptoms in plants are very difficult to observe. In commercial plantings the symptoms are seldom so clearly defined as they are in controlled tests in which extreme differences in
mineral nutrition are used. It may be possible to recognize the symptoms of iron deficiency in some plants caused by an actual lack of iron
in the soil or by too high pH. Yellow terminal leaves are an indication
of iron deficiency in plants—in some plants the leaves will be entirely
yellow, and in others the veins may remain green. Boron deficiency in
carnation plants produces characteristic symptoms in terminal growth
that are rather easy to recognize, but the symptoms in other plants
are not so clearly defined. It is difficult to determine phosphorus and
calcium deficiencies in the soil by observing plant growth, and the
symptoms of potassium deficiency are not definite except in extreme
conditions. Some growers feel that they can sense deficiencies in potassium by weak stems; but this is questionable, because this symptom is
closely related to other environmental conditions that may be even
more responsible for the type of growth.

In determining soil fertility by means of inspecting plant growth
and development, a reliable point of reference is indispensable. Is
the leaf size, leaf color, and rate and type of growth really a variation
from the norm or is it imagined? Careful comparisons should be made

with other plants at the same stage of growth in the same greenhouse range or with plants in other greenhouses in the area. Sometimes
the point of reference can be records that have been kept on prior
crops, or written descriptions or illustrations in books or manuals.
Without using a good point of reference from time to time, it is easy
to come to the wrong conclusion about the status of mineral nutrition
in soil and plant.

● THERE ARE SEVERAL METHODS FOR TESTING SOIL

The greenhouse manager does have a need for evaluation of the
fertility of the soil. It would be convenient if there were one accepted
method of soil analysis, but there are many and the results seem to be
at great variance. The two primary considerations with soil testing
are the reliability of the service and the speed with which it can be
handled. In evaluating reliability it must be determined first that the
service does handle greenhouse flower and plant soils. If it does, have
the recommendations based on its tests produced consistently good
results? The soil testing service not only must report values but must
interpret these results and make recommendations for the proper action
to take.

The results and recommendations from the test must be known
in the shortest possible time—a week would be desirable, two weeks
might be acceptable, but usually three weeks would make the service
useless. A certain amount of time is involved in testing and evaluating,
regardless of where the test is made, but time in transit may be reduced
by using the closest service.

If timely soil testing is not a possibility, then the grower had better
develop his own service. The equipment he would use may not be the
same as that used at an established testing service, but the recommendations based on the tests should be very similar. In starting his
own service he should send half of each soil sample to a reliable soil
testing service and then compare recommendations. Regardless of
whether he does his own soil testing or uses an established service, the
grower must have a Solu Bridge for making total fertilizer (soluble
salts or salts) determinations rapidly. The equipment is indispensable.

The Solu Bridge may be used for trouble shooting. As noted

earlier, it sometimes is difficult to tell if a plant growth symptom is caused by an excess or a deficiency of mineral nutrients. This can be evaluated accurately by the Solu Bridge in a matter of minutes. It may be used routinely on a regular basis to detect needed adjustments in the fertilizer program. No, the Solu Bridge cannot replace a complete soil testing service, but because of the speed with which it can be used it is a valuable addition to it.

Regardless of the soil testing method used, the soil sample must be typical of the entire mass of soil in question. If it is a bench of soil, the usually accepted procedure is to remove about ½ inch of the surface and then take a core for the entire depth of the soil. This is done at four to six locations the length of the bench, and the cores are then combined in a single sample. If there is variable growth in the same bench, the soil from the poor areas should be sampled separately from the soil from the good areas so that a comparison can be made. The procedure for pot plants is quite different. They are relatively short-term crops, and it can be assumed that if the nutrient status is suitable at the time of potting and an acceptable fertilizer program is used, no soil testing may be required. If soil analysis is indicated, it might be best to sacrifice a plant or two and make the sample from the entire potful of soil.

The soil testing services may report different results for the same soil sample because they use different methods of making the soil solution, use different testing methods, or report in different terms. This in no way means that one service is wrong and another is right, but it should be understood that the evaluation of the test and recommendations for action to be taken must be made by the individuals who are qualified to know the meaning of the tests and the results. The tests are made on a solution made from the soil sample that is submitted. It is assumed that the interest is in knowing the quantity of material present in the soil sample that would be available for diffusion into the plant root. The various individuals who have devised soil testing procedures have had different concepts of the proper extracting solution to use. The general belief is that the typical soil solution in the vicinity of the roots contains some dissolved substances in water; so, in making the extract from the soil sample, they attempt to use a similar solution.

Because of the differences in the extracting solutions which are used, there may be some differences in the amounts of nutrient minerals dissolved from the soil sample.

There is more than one way to determine the presence and quantity of minerals in the soil extract, and the results will not necessarily be the same.

Most of the testing procedures used for flower greenhouse soils report the results in parts per million (ppm)—but this may be ppm in the extract or it may be ppm in the soil sample, or in other instances it may be in index values. Some of the testing procedures used for field crop soils and garden soils report the results in pounds per acre. One soil testing service reports some of the results in terms of parts per 10 million.

Regardless of the methods used and the terms of the report, the final judgment given by each testing service should be approximately the same. It is possible that one soil testing service may report the nitrates in a soil sample as 25 ppm while another service may report 100 ppm on the same sample, and yet they may both make the same judgement that the nitrate quantity in the soil is adequate to high and recommend no further addition of nitrates. This situation is not too different from an individual going to two different medical doctors who make various tests and report in different terms, yet give a similar diagnosis or judgement in the end.

It would be convenient if there were a standard soil testing procedure used throughout the country, but until this does occur each grower must choose the soil testing service that he believes is reliable and gives prompt reports, and then have sufficient faith to follow the recommendations. If a suitable soil testing service is not available in the locality and it is desired to make the tests right at the greenhouse, the Simplex Soil Testing Outfits can give reliable results when properly used.

Tests on soils used for flower and plant production in the greenhouse should determine the pH, nitrates, phosphorus, potassium, calcium, and total soluble salts. On some occasions it is desired to know the status of other minerals, and tests on manganese, magnesium, or ammonium may be made.

The soil test reports for bench or bed soils should be transferred to an accumulative record by each bench. The soil test record for each bench will have columns for date of test, pH, nitrates, phosphorus, potassium, calcium, soluble salts, recommended action, and action taken with date. As the entries are made each test date, the results for the previous tests can be compared with them readily. Unless there has been an obvious reason for it there should be little or no change in the results reported for phosphorus and calcium from test to test. The pH value may remain quite constant, or it may drift in one direction slowly. An abrupt change in pH should not be expected unless a considerable addition of an acid or base substance had been made to the soil to cause it. Depending on type of soil, crop, irrigation methods, and possibly other factors, significant changes could be expected in results for nitrates, potassium, and soluble salts. If little or no fertilizer has been added to the soil between tests, it could be expected that all three values would be lower. Because of the anticipated loss of nitrates and potassium from the soil, the routine fertilizer program often is based on additions of those two minerals in quantities that should maintain adequate amounts in the soil. The soil test results will verify if the fertilizer program has been adequate or if adjustment is needed.

Although adjustments should not need to be made regularly for pH and calcium, they do have to be made far enough in advance because the corrective effect is also slow. If it is apparent from inspecting the soil test record sheet for the bench that there has been a continuous drift in pH or calcium, action should be taken before the critical stage is reached. It is rather easy to make these adjustments between crops, but it may be very difficult after the crop is planted. If the soil test record is compiled for each bench, the trend will be evident and the action to be taken between crops clearly indicated.

When should soil tests be made? Well, they should be made frequently enough so that the mineral nutrients needed by the plants will be present in proper amounts at all times. This is a sometime thing. There will be some instances in which testing once a month will be rather wasteful of time, and there will be other situations in which testing once a week may not be quite often enough. The manager will need to exercise his judgement. There does not seem to be any excuse for not testing each bench of soil and each batch of potting soil before planting. Then corrective action may be taken before planting, and the fertilizer program can be planned based on the anticipated mineral nutrient requirements for the duration of the crop. With pot plants, it may be suitable to withhold further testing until a problem is indicated. With bench and bed crops, the best estimate might be to test each bench after a month and then test on a monthly basis until the accumulated record indicates that the mineral status and the fertilizer program are stable enough to warrant less frequent testing. With judicious use of the Solu Bridge, it should be possible to limit the number of complete soil tests considerably.

● **PRE-PLANTING TESTS SHOULD INCLUDE DETERMINATION
OF SOIL DRAINAGE CHARACTERISTICS**

The soil tests made before planting should include the test that determines the soil drainage characteristics (See Fig. 5-3.) as well as the test for mineral nutrients. This also applies to the base soil for pot plants. These tests will indicate the quantity of organic matter which should be incorporated into the soil as it is mixed. After mixing, the drainage tests should be made again in order to determine if the right amount of additive was used.

If new soil is being used in bench or bed, the same testing procedure as was used with the pot soil should be followed. Frequently bench and bed soils are continued in use crop after crop, and because of this a continuous record of the status of mineral nutrients will be maintained. These tests will indicate what fertilizers should be incorporated into the soil before the next crop is planted; however, the drainage test should be made on the soil after the plants are removed in order to determine the amount of organic matter to add. Of the mineral nutrients it is primarily the calcium and phosphorus that should be handled before the crop is planted; but if adjustment in pH or soluble salts is needed, it should be done at that time also.

● **THE MINERAL NUTRIENT STATUS IN THE PLANT MAY BE DETERMINED BY
LABORATORY PROCEDURES COMMONLY CALLED FOLIAR ANALYSIS**

Situations arise in which it would be helpful to know just what the mineral status is in the plant, and procedures have been developed for determining this by testing portions of the plant—usually leaves. This type of plant analysis is used primarily as a research tool or for trouble shooting. Sometimes it is used to find the quantity of one or more minerals in the plant for which there is no established method for soil testing.

If it appears that foliar analysis is needed, the state extension specialist should be able to produce the information on where and how it is done. There are relatively few states that have this type of testing service, but those that do may have an arrangement for handling samples out of their state.

● **FERTILIZERS SUPPLY THE MINERAL NUTRIENTS
   REQUIRED BY PLANTS**

A brief discussion on the terms and language used in reference to mineral nutrients and fertilizers could clear up a few points. In general talk on this subject, the name of the element is used in a generic sense. In some instances the reference will be to the element form, and at other times the element name will be used when referring to compounds or ions containing that element. Many chemical elements are required by plants. The ones, however, with which we are repeatedly involved are nitrogen (N), phosphorus (P), potassium (K), and calcium (Ca).

Fertilizers are chemical compounds and mixtures of chemical compounds. The common nitrogen fertilizers are ammonium nitrate (NH_4NO_3), ammonium sulfate ($(NH_4)_2SO_4$), sodium nitrate ($NaNO_3$), potassium nitrate (KNO_3), urea (NH_2CONH_2), calcium nitrate ($Ca(NO_3)_2$), and di-ammonium phosphate ($(NH_4)_2HPO_4$). It is apparent that other than urea the nitrogen fertilizers are either ammonium or nitrate compounds.

Superphosphate is probably the most common phosphorus fertilizer used. It is a mixture of monocalcium phosphate ($Ca(H_2PO_4)_2$) and calcium sulfate ($CaSO_4$). Superphosphate is used only for dry application. Monocalcium phosphate and di-ammonium phosphate are water soluble and are used sometimes for liquid applications of phosphorus fertilizer.

Potassium nitrate is used as a source of potassium fertilizer for liquid application. Potassium chloride (KCL) and potassium sulfate (K_2SO_4) are used more commonly in fertilizers for dry application.

The two calcium compounds which make up superphosphate (monocalcium phosphate and calcium sulfate) are fertilizer sources for calcium. Other calcium compounds used as fertilizers are agricultural limestone ($CaCO_3$), dolomite (an equimolecular mixture of $CaCO_3$ and $MgCO_3$) or dolomitic limestone which is a variable mixture of calcium and magnesium carbonates, gypsum ($CaSO_4$), hydrated lime ($Ca(OH)_2$), and calcium nitrate, listed before as a nitrogen fertilizer.

In the soil solution the various fertilizer compounds dissociate into the ions of which they are composed, and it is the ions which may enter the plant through the roots—nitrogen as the nitrate (NO_3-) or ammonium (NH_4+) ions; phosphorus as phosphoric acid ions (H_2PO_4-) or (HPO_4--); potassium as ($K+$) and calcium as ($Ca++$). The positively charged ions are called cations and the negatively charged ones anions.

To further confuse things a bit, label registration for fertilizers requires that the quantity of nitrogen, phosphorus, and potassium in the fertilizer in per cent by weight be declared; and because of testing procedures used in the past, nitrogen is reported as the element (N), but phosphorus as (P_2O_5) and potassium as (K_2O). A fertilizer of analysis 25-5-20 then is 25 per cent nitrogen expressed as (N), 5 per cent phosphorus expressed as (P_2O_5), and 20 per cent potassium expressed as (K_2O). In more recent years there has been some interest in changing label registration so that all minerals are expressed as the element, and in some areas this has been done. Under the new plan the analysis that was 25-5-20 would then be 25-2.2-16.6. This can be something of a shocker because it has been popular to call fertilizers such as 20-20-20 "balanced fertilizers," and under the new plan the analysis would be 20-8.8-16.6. The fertilizer is no less balanced than it ever was, but this should illustrate that the term was improper or meaningless in the first place.

To convert from an analysis in terms of P_2O_5 to P, multiply by 0.44;

or to convert from P to P_2O_5, multiply by 2.29. For an analysis in terms of K_2O to K, multiply by 0.83; or K to K_2O, multiply by 1.2.

The mixed or prepared fertilizers are mixtures of chemical compounds in proportions to produce the amounts of mineral nutrients that are desired to be applied to the soil. Some of these prepared fertilizers are for dry application, and they may or may not be made with compounds which are completely water soluble. They are commonly called low analysis fertilizers because the total declared analysis N, P, and K is 20 per cent or less. In many of these prepared fertilizers, superphosphate is used as the source of phosphorus, ammonium sulfate or other ammonium compounds as the source of nitrogen, and potassium chloride for the potassium source.

The prepared fertilizers for liquid application must be made from compounds that are completely water soluble. These are high analysis fertilizers with total declared analysis of 30 per cent to 60 per cent. They are made from such compounds as ammonium nitrate, di-ammonium phosphate, potassium nitrate, or urea for the nitrogen sources, and phosphorus may be obtained from di-ammonium phosphate and the potassium from the potassium nitrate. The high analysis fertilizers frequently are made with chelated trace elements incorporated and also with a dye mixed uniformly throughout the fertilizer so that the presence of the fertilizer is apparent in the irrigation water.

Some of the mixed or prepared fertilizers have properties of limited or controlled solubility. They are commonly referred to as *slow release fertilizers*. Some are made from organic compounds, and the mineral nutrients become available as these organics decompose. Some mineral nutrients are combined in glass-like frits which are only slightly soluble, so small amounts of the minerals are available over a long period of time. In the slow release fertilizer called *Osmocote*, the fertilizer granules are encapsuled in plastic, which limits the rate of diffusion of the minerals. One type of coating which is used provides diffusion for about three months, and the other type for about nine months. MagAmp is a mixture of two compounds (magnesium ammonium phosphate and magnesium potassium phosphate) that are slightly water soluble. The medium grade dissolves over a

period of about three months, and the coarse grade may require about
two years to dissolve completely.

- ## THE REQUIRED MINERALS MUST GET INTO
  ## THE PLANT IN THE RIGHT AMOUNTS

To accomplish this, the soil, irrigation, and fertilizer must be managed properly. The choice of kind, amount, and method of application
of fertilizer must be based on the need for minerals in the plant and
the best way to get them there. The mineral nutrients enter the plant
through the roots if they are in active growth, so the number one concern must be maintaining continuous root growth. The best fertilizer
program is of no avail if the fertilizer has no means of entrance into
the plant. Except in some extreme situations, lack of fertilizer does not
limit root growth, but too much fertilizer may severely damage roots.
The manager will have to look at the roots as often as he does soil
test reports in order to be able to establish the fertilizer program. This
is something that cannot be done by a machine or a testing service. The
manager has to be in charge of maintaining the good root system of the
plant and should coordinate all of the soil management activities toward that end.

If root growth is good and active, this is evidence that (1) the
soil drainage is adequate, (2) root pests and diseases are not a problem, (3) there is not too much fertilizer, and (4) frequency and
amount of irrigation have been about right. If root growth is not good,
one or more of these may be the cause, and root growth (and mineral
movement into the plant) will not improve until these causes are corrected.

The availability of minerals in the soil varies with the reaction
(pH), and the fertilizer program must provide for adjustment of the
pH within acceptable limits. It is unusual for pH to change abruptly.
If soil pH is changing, the direction in which it is going will be
evident in the accumulated soil test reports. Action to change the drift
in pH should be taken before it reaches the critical stage. The soil pH
for many greenhouse crops should be about 6.5. Soil pH of 6.0 is certainly acceptable and pH 5.5 may not even be a problem, but it is on
the borderline. The point is that if the pH progression is slowly but

steadily downward from 6.5, some adjustment needs to be made in the fertilizer program soon enough to reverse this trend before it reaches a critical stage. At the upper end of the scale pH 7.0 may be acceptable and 7.5 may not really present a problem, but the fertilizer program should be changed when the trend becomes evident, rather than a critical stage being waited for before action is taken.

Regulation of soil pH should be attempted before the crop is planted. Agricultural limestone should be the best material to add to the soil to make it more alkaline; however, hydrated lime may be used when faster action is desired. Either of these may be used at 5 pounds per 100 square feet of soil or at 2½ pounds per cubic yard. Quite often more than one application is required. In such situations it would help to use either sodium nitrate or calcium nitrate as the nitrogen source in the fertilizer program also, as either one has an alkaline reaction.

To make the soil more acid, sulfur may be added at the rate of about 3 pounds per 100 square feet or 1½ pounds per cubic yard, or iron (ferrous) sulfate at one pound per 100 square feet or ½ pound per cubic yard. Be sure that it is ferrous sulfate and not ferric sulfate. The ammonium fertilizers have an acid reaction in the soil and can be used in the fertilizer program to lower pH.

- **WHEN ROOT GROWTH IS GOOD AND SOIL pH SUITABLE, PLANTS WILL REACT READILY TO AN ADEQUATE FERTILIZER PROGRAM**

The best program for most growers probably is to know the fertilizer status of the soil at the time the crop is planted and then add enough fertilizer periodically to take care of the needs of the crop. It is practical to add phosphorus and calcium if they are needed to the soil before the crop is planted. For phosphorus, superphosphate is used at the rate of 5 pounds per 100 square feet or 2½ pounds per cubic yard. This also will add calcium to the soil. If lime was added to the soil to raise the pH, this would also increase the calcium content. When neither lime or superphosphate is added to the soil but some calcium is needed, gypsum (calcium sulfate) should be applied at the rate of 5 pounds per 100 square feet or 2½ pounds per cubic yard.

If the program includes the use of slowly available fertilizers, they should be incorporated into the soil before planting. It is possible to use them for the sole source of minerals for the crop, or as a supplement to the regular program.

For the regular fertilizer program, there is good reason to apply some fertilizer with each irrigation. The utilization or loss of minerals from the soil is somewhat comparable to that of water, and this provides a routine for making the fertilizer application. If handled properly, the frequent but small applications of minerals should provide the uniform source of nutrients required by plants. In practice it works out quite well with some possible adjustment of the program needed at the start of the crop and during the winter. If the soil is devoid of nitrogen at planting time, some additional nitrogen should be used for the first week or so. During the cold and dark weather in winter, the irrigations are so infrequent that insufficient minerals will be supplied at that time unless the concentration of fertilizer in the irrigation water is increased or some fertilizer is supplied in a different way. Some of the slow release fertilizers may be used at both of these times to take care of those needs.

Soils which are coarse, porous, and well drained may be watered heavily, and for general purposes the irrigation water should contain about 200 ppm nitrogen (as N) and 200 ppm potassium (as K). Using an injector with 1:100 proportion, 11.0 ounces of 25-0-25 analysis fertilizer per gallon of concentrate water would supply 200 ppm nitrogen (N) and 166 ppm potassium (K) in the irrigation water. Prepared fertilizers often have rate of use on the label.

Soils that do not drain well must not be watered so heavily nor have so much fertilizer applied. Such soils are difficult to manage in the greenhouse, and it is strongly recommended that they be mixed with enough organic matter to make them well drained in greenhouse conditions. Good crops may be grown in heavy, slowly drained soils, but it requires the close, personal supervision of a grower who thoroughly understands the requirements.

- ### WITH SOME ATTENTION TO DETAILS THE GROWER CAN MIX HIS OWN FERTILIZERS

The prepared mixed fertilizers are excellent and certainly a convenience to use. There probably is a greater array of analyses than there is need for. There is no need for a different analysis fertilizer for each crop. Most greenhouse soils are well supplied with phosphorus through continual use, or else superphosphate is applied before the crop is planted; so phosphorus should not be applied during the growth of the crop. In prepared fertilizers most greenhouse operators should use analyses such as 25-0-25, 20-5-30, or 25-5-20, rather than 20-20-20, because their soils already contain enough or too much phosphorus.

It is possible for a grower to mix his own fertilizers. The backbone of do-it-yourself mixed fertilizers is potassium nitrate, 13-0-44. It may be used by itself, but for most situations that would be supplying too much potassium per unit of nitrogen. Either ammonium nitrate (33-0-0) or calcium nitrate (15-0-0) may be mixed with potassium nitrate to increase the percentage of nitrogen in the mixture. When one part of ammonium nitrate (33-0-0) is used with one part of potassium nitrate (13-0-44), the analysis of the mixture is about 23-0-22:

$$\frac{(33\text{-}0\text{-}0) + (13\text{-}0\text{-}44)}{2} = \frac{46\text{-}0\text{-}44}{2} = 23\text{-}0\text{-}22.$$

To use this mixture at the rate of 12 ounces of 23-0-22 fertilizer per gallon of concentrate water, 6 ounces of ammonium nitrate and 6 ounces of potassium nitrate would be placed in the gallon of water. It is not practical for most growers to attempt to mix dry fertilizers together because it is difficult to get a uniform mix. The mix will be reliable, however, when the proper amount of each is placed into the water and then mixed.

For a mixture of approximately 14-0-15 analysis, one part potassium nitrate can be used with two parts calcium nitrate:

$$\frac{(13\text{-}0\text{-}44) + (15\text{-}0\text{-}0) + (15\text{-}0\text{-}0)}{3} = \frac{43\text{-}0\text{-}44}{3} = 14\text{-}0\text{-}15.$$

This mixture would supply some calcium as well as nitrogen and potassium, and the reaction would be basic rather than acid. To use this 14-0-15 fertilizer at the rate of 18 ounces per gallon concentrate water, 6 ounces of potassium nitrate and 12 ounces of calcium nitrate would be placed into the water and mixed.

To make a fertilizer containing nitrogen, phosphorus, and potassium, it probably would be best to use a mixture of potassium nitrate, ammonium nitrate, and di-ammonium phosphate (21-53-0). With equal parts of each the analysis would be about 22-18-15:

$$\frac{(13\text{-}0\text{-}44) + (33\text{-}0\text{-}0) + (21\text{-}53\text{-}0)}{3} = \frac{67\text{-}53\text{-}44}{3} = 22\text{-}18\text{-}15.$$

To use this 22-18-15 mixture at the rate of 12 ounces per gallon of concentrate, 4 ounces of each would be added to the water.

In doing your own fertilizer mixes, it should be kept in mind that there will be no color trace in these mixtures unless you add it, and it may be lacking in some trace elements provided in the prepared mixture.

● FERTILIZERS MUST BE APPLIED UNIFORMLY TO THE SOIL

Regardless of the method of application, the result must be uniform. When the fertilizer is being incorporated into the soil before planting, the soil must be worked so thoroughly that the fertilizer is uniformly distributed throughout.

Applying dry fertilizer to the soil after planting is difficult. The problems are to distribute it evenly over the soil without getting it on the plants. It requires some dedicated individuals to accomplish this. At the points where fertilizer comes in contact with the plant, water diffuses out of the plant tissue to the fertilizer and the tissue is destroyed, leaving blemished areas or in some cases entirely destroyed leaves or stems. If dry application must be made, it should be followed immediately with syringing of the plants. It is even more difficult to apply dry fertilizers to pot plants than to plants in benches or beds. The soil should be moist at the time of dry fertilizer application and then should be irrigated after the application. Failure to do this frequently results in damage to roots because of direct contact of roots with the fertilizer granules—loss of water from the root tissue to the fertilizer, with dehydration and permanent damage to the tissues.

Applying fertilizer in the liquid form is by far the best method when it can be used, as it is much easier to apply uniformly and much labor is saved. The first method used for liquid application of fertilizer was to mix the fertilizer in a tank of water and pump directly from there to the soil. These systems were designed for periodic use rather than for each irrigation. In such a situation, a 20 per cent nitrogen fertilizer would be used at the rate of 3 pounds per 100 gallons of water (about 720 ppm), and application would be made about every two weeks. In the period of time since then, soil mixtures have been made more coarse and porous; and with these soils, applications would need to be more frequent.

Various siphoning devices have been designed for adding fertilizer concentrate to irrigation water, but these are nearly worthless because of variable results.

The positive displacement injectors are very reliable, and when properly used will give excellent results. These units are designed for adding a small amount of fertilizer concentrate to the irrigation water— about the amount needed with each irrigation—, so they must be used that way rather than for periodic applications of fertilizer. Most of the units require clean water for trouble-free operation. Water with silt or sand in it will cause undue wear.

The minimum and maximum rate of water flow for irrigation needs to be known in order to get the right size injector. Injectors large enough to handle the maximum flow of water may not be entirely accurate if the minimum demand is too low. An injector small enough to handle minimum water flows may wear rapidly if operated at rates greater than its maximum.

- **ALL ASPECTS OF THE SITUATION MUST BE EVALUATED WHEN PLANT PROBLEMS ARE ANALYZED**

Soil and/or plant tissue tests may be an essential part of the analysis when there appears to be trouble in plant growth or development, but they must be evaluated along with other pertinent events and factors.

Reference Reviews

1. Anonymous, *Commercial Production of Pot Plants*, Bulletin 112, Her Majesty's Stationery Office, London, 1969. *The sections on composting soils, irrigating, and use of fertilizers as recommended in Great Britain are of interest.*

2. Anonymous, *A Manual of Carnation Production*, Bulletin 151, Her Majesty's Stationery Office, London, 1967. *There is no discussion of soils included, but it does cover soil sterilization, watering, nutrition, and soil-less culture.*

3. Baker, Kenneth F. et al., *The U. C. System for Producing Healthy Container-Grown Plants*, Manual 23, California Agricultural Experiment Station-Extension Service, Berkeley, 1957. *An excellent reference book on soil management for growers in any location. The soil mixes may or may not be of interest to each individual, but there is a wealth of information on plant pathogens in the soil, treating soils with heat or chemicals, and methods of handling soils.*

4. Ecke, Paul, Jr., and O. A. Matkin, *The Poinsettia Manual*, Paul Ecke Poinsettias, Encinitas, California, 1971. *Although this manual was written for a single crop, the information on soils, irrigation, mineral nutrition, and soil pests and diseases has general application.*

5. Holley, W. D., *Bulletin*, Colorado Flower Growers Association, Inc., Fort Collins, Colorado. *This bulletin is published regularly and reports the work of Prof. Holley, his associates, and his students. Much of the work has been done in relation to carnations, but most of the work in soils, irrigation, and mineral nutrition published in the past has general application.*

6. Holley, W. D., and Ralph Baker, *Carnation Production*, William C. Brown Company, Inc., Dubuque, Iowa, 1963. *Chapter 7, "Nutrient and Water Relations," discusses soil management with specific reference to carnations.*

7. Kohnke, Helmut, *Soil Physics*, McGraw-Hill Book Company, New York, 1968. *This is easier reading and more understandable to the greenhouse grower than the title would suggest. A fine book for the individual who is interested in understanding the science behind soil management.*

8. Langhans, Robert W., et al., *Carnations—A Manual of the Culture, Insects and Diseases, and Economics of Carnations*, New York State Extension Service, Ithaca, 1961. *Soil management for this crop is given in Chapter 3, "Soil Preparation," Chapter 6, "Fertilization," and Chapter 7, "Watering."*

9. Langhans, Robert W. et al., *Chrysanthemums—A Manual of the Culture, Diseases, Insects, and Economics of Chrysanthemums*, New York State Extension Service and New York State Flower Growers Association, Inc., Ithica, 1964. *Chapters 8 through 10 discuss soil management and may be helpful. Section II, "Disease and Insects," contains a thorough and clear presentation of this subject.*

10. Langhans, Robert W., et al., *Snapdragons—A Manual of the Culture, Insects and Diseases, and Economics of Snapdragons*, New York Extension Service, Ithaca, 1962. *Chapter 4, "Soil Preparation," Chapter 6, "Fertilization," Chapter 7, "Watering," Chapter 11, "Soil Sterlization and*

Root Rots," and Chapter 13, "Insects," all are concerned with soil management, but chapters 7 and 11 may be of most interest.

11. Langhans, Robert W., and D. C. Kiplinger, *Easter Lilies–The Culture, Diseases, Insects, and Economics of Easter Lilies,* New York State Extension Service, Ithaca, and Cooperative Extension Service, Ohio State University, Columbus, 1967. *Chapter 7, "Soils and Fertilizers," discusses some of the specifics for lilies, but Chapter 8, "Watering," gives general information which would apply to most pot plant crops. Section II includes information on diseases, viruses, and insects.*

12. Langhans, Robert W., and James W. Boodley, *Bulletin,* New York State Flower Growers, Inc., Ithaca. *This bulletin is published regularly, and several of the issues from November 1961 through August 1963 report on the exhaustive soil study by Hanan and others. There are summary articles on soil management by Spomer and Langhans in the bulletins published in 1968.*

13. Laurie, Alex, D. C. Kiplinger, and Kennard S. Nelson, *Commercial Flower Forcing,* Seventh Edition, McGraw-Hill Book Company, New York, 1969. *Soils and fertilizers are treated completely in chapters 6 and 7. Irrigation is covered in Chapter 5, and the general discussion on pests and diseases is in Chapter 9. In addition, comments and recommendations for specific crops are given for each crop in chapters 10 through 12.*

14. Mastalerz, John W., et al., *Geraniums–A Manual on the Culture, Diseases, Insects, Economics, Taxonomy, and Breeding of Geraniums,* Second Edition, Pennsylvania Flower Growers, University Park, 1971. *Although the title of this manual is specific, the sections referring to soil management provide information that pertains to most greenhouse crops. Chapter 5, "Growing Media," Chapter 6, "Soil Treatment with Steam or Chemicals," Chapter 7, "Irrigation," and Chapter 8, "Fertilization," all present the subject very effectively. Chapters 19 through 26 on diseases and Chapter 27 on insects contain specific references to geranium problems but also a wealth of information for general application.*

15. Mastalerz, John W., and Robert W. Langhans, *Roses–A Manual on the Culture, Management, Diseases, Insects, Economics, and Breeding of Greenhouse Roses,* Pennsylvania Flower Growers, University Park, New York State Flower Growers Association, Inc., Ithaca, and Roses, Inc., Haslett, Michigan, 1969. *Various aspects of soil management are covered in the following chapters in this manual: Chapter 6, "Growing Media," Chapter 7, "Soil Aeration," Chapter 8, "Soil Treatment," Chap-12, "Water Requirements and Irrigation Practices," Chapter 13, "Fertilization," Chapter 14, "Mulches," Chapter 21, "Weed Control," Chapter 26, "Root and Stem Diseases," Chapter 27, "Nematode Problems," and Chapter 29, "Soil Insects and Related Pests."*

16. Millar, C. E., L. M. Turk, and H. D. Foth, *Fundamentals of Soil Science,* Fourth Edition, John Wiley & Sons, Inc., New York, 1966. *The soil de-*

scribed here is naturally derived soil, and the crops are agronomic or
field crops; this is well discussed by the authors. Many of the concepts are valid for greenhouse soils, and others need to be modified because of the way greenhouse soils are handled, the difference in outdoors and indoors environment, cultural methods that are used in the
greenhouse, and the variance in requirements for greenhouse and field
crops.

17. Miller, Robert O., D. C. Kiplinger, et al., *Poinsettias*, Extension Bulletin
S. B. 15, Ohio State University, Columbus, 1963. *Chapter 7, "Soils, Fertilizers, and Watering," covers soil management for poinsettias.*

18. Nelson, Kennard S., *Flower and Plant Production in the Greenhouse*,
The Interstate Printers & Publishers, Inc., Danville, Illinois, 1967. *Soil
management is presented in Chapter 4, "Soil, Fertilizers, and Irrigation,"
and specific applications are covered in Chapter 6, "Cut Flower Crops,"
and Chapter 7, "Pot Plant Crops." Soil pests and diseases are included in
Chapter 8, "Troubles, Pests, and Diseases." The glossary at the end
of the book will be helpful to new growers.*

19. Salisbury, Frank B., and Cleon Ross, *Plant Physiology*, Wadsworth Publishing Company, Inc., Belmont, California, 1969. *The greenhouse grower does not have to be a plant physiologist, but it certainly helps him in
his work if he does have an acquaintance with the basics of the subject.
These two authors handle the subject well. It might not be a book that
every grower will be able to read from cover to cover, but there are
many sections that will be interesting and helpful. For a better understanding of soil management an acquaintance with the following chapters is suggested: Chapter 2, "The Water Milieu," Chapter 5, "Osmosis
and the Components of Water Potential," Chapter 6, "Transpiration and
Heat Transfer," and Chapter 10, "Mineral Nutrition of Plants."*

20. Tisdale, Samuel L., and Werner L. Nelson, *Soil Fertility and Fertilizers*,
Second Edition, The Macmillan Company, New York, 1966. *The information in this book is for naturally derived soils and agronomic or field
crops. Some concepts apply directly to greenhouse soils, methods, and
crops; others do not fit well because of the difference in conditions. However, it is all good background information.*

CHAPTER 6

Management of the Greenhouse
Air Environment

CHAPTER 6

There are some local variations, but the earth's atmosphere is a surprisingly uniform mixture of gases consisting approximately of 78 per cent nitrogen, 21 per cent oxygen, 1 per cent argon, and 0.03 per cent carbon dioxide. If air flow is not impeded, these proportions of gases in the air mixture remain quite constant. Air usually contains water vapor, and the quantity varies considerably.

Light reaches the plants through the air. It is absorbed, reflected, or transmitted directly by plant tissues. The amount and kind of light which enters the plant is controlled by the pigments in the plant. There is some exchange of air or its components directly through plant tissues, but the primary route of exchange is via the plant pores known as stomates. This in no way is a breathing action in which volumes of air are taken into the leaf through the stomates and other volumes of gases exhausted from the plant through the stomates. It is a process of diffusion in which the various gases making up the air may act individually, with the direction of diffusion through the stomate determined by the difference in concentration of that particular gas inside and outside the leaf. The practical result is that the amount of oxygen, or carbon dioxide, or water vapor diffusing into or out of the leaf will vary from time to time, depending on the concentration of each of these gases in the plant tissues and in the air.

The amount of diffusion also depends on whether the stomates are open or closed. Very little interchange of gases occurs when the stomates are closed. Several factors affect the opening of stomates. Plant stomates will be open when the tissues are turgid because of sufficient water in them; the light intensity is 100 to 300 foot-candles or more; the concentration of carbon dioxide within the plant is low; and the temperature is below 85° to 95°F. If there is a water stress (water deficiency) within the plant, the stomates may close in spite of a low concentration of carbon dioxide in the plant or a high level of light intensity available for the plant. The opening of the stomates is not controlled by the concentration of carbon dioxide in the atmosphere outside of the plant, but the rate of diffusion of carbon dioxide into the plant is directly related to the difference in concentration outside and inside the leaf.

The traffic that is of most concern through the stomates is the diffusion inward of carbon dioxide, the movement of oxygen in or out depending on the concentration of it within the plant, and the diffusion outward of water vapor in transpiration. An adequate supply of carbon dioxide within the plant is vital for the plant's food manufacturing process, photosynthesis; and conveniently the stomate opening is triggered by low carbon dioxide concentration within the plant, allowing the supply to be replenished. The rate of opening of stomates and the degree of opening are directly related to the intensity of light—the more intense the light, the faster and wider the stomates open; and thus the area through which carbon dioxide may diffuse into the plant is increased in bright light when the rate of food manufacture may be the greatest.

Oxygen is a by-product of photosnythesis, and at times the concentration of oxygen within the plant will be sufficient so that it diffuses through the stomates to the atmosphere outside the leaf. At other times the concentration of oxygen within the plant may be lower than in the air surrounding the plant, and oxygen may diffuse in through the stomates. It is essential to have an adequate oxygen supply to support respiration in the plant.

Water vapor diffusion from the plant through the stomates to the atmosphere around the plant is known as transpiration. This involves not only water removal from the plant but heat loss, because as water changes from the liquid phase within the plant to the vapor phase which diffuses through the stomates, about 600 calories of heat leave the plant with every gram of water—or, if you will, about 8,800 British thermal units of heat with every gallon of water. This is an essential procedure for regulation of plant temperature, and it follows that a wilted plant is also a hot plant—quite possibly an overheated plant, in which respiration proceeds too rapidly, depleting food in the plant, and causing some general deterioration if the wilting (and overheating) is allowed to continue.

● PLANTS CAN BE AFFECTED BY RADIANT ENERGY

We are inclined to think only of the light visible to us as being radiant energy. Visible light is electromagnetic radiation, but it is a very small portion of that total radiation. The spectrum of electromagnetic radiation ranges from cosmic rays to radio waves, and the most common reference to this radiation is by wavelength. Visible light is at about the middle of the spectrum. The shortest wave length is cosmic rays, which are about 1/100,000,000 the size of visible light rays; gamma rays are about 1/1,000,000 the size, X rays about 1/10,000, and ultraviolet rays about 1/100; infrared rays are about 100 times larger, and radio waves about 100,000,000 times larger.

It is not known what effects cosmic rays may have on plants. Both gamma rays and X rays may be used by the plant breeder to change the genetic characteristics of plants. Ultraviolet rays have no known beneficial effects on plants. Infrared rays increase the temperature of plant tissues and may affect various processes that occur in plants. Radio waves have no known effects on plants, but there has been speculation of some relationships. The electromagnetic radiation at about the middle of the spectrum (visible light) has profound effects on plants, and that will be covered in some detail later.

Because of the great difference in size of wavelength in electromagnetic radiation, terminology varies with the size unit chosen to describe the wavelength. Toward the middle of the spectrum it is common to use millimicron ($m\mu$). A micron is 1/1,000,000 of a meter, and a millimicron is 1/1,000 of a micron. More recently this value has been called nanometer (nm), and that term is used in the following discussions. In the past, wavelengths of this order also were referred to in terms of Angstrom units (A); but because an A is 1/10 the size of a $m\mu$ 1,000 A = 100 $m\mu$—or 1,000 A = 100 nm.

Of the electromagnetic radiation which originates at the sun, only a portion of it reaches the earth's surface, because of screening by some portions of the atmosphere. The wavelengths of sunrays that strike the earth's surface range from about 310 to 2,300 nm. The portion of the electromagnetic spectrum visible to human beings is from 390 to 760 nm. The shortest visible rays (around 400 nm) we recognize as violet-colored light, and the colors that we perceive gradually change with increase in wavelength of the radiation from violet to blue at about 450 nm, to green at about 500 nm, to yellow at about 550 nm, to orange at around 600 nm, to red around 650 nm, and to far red at around 700 nm.

- ### GREEN PLANTS HAVE THE UNIQUE ABILITY TO CONVERT LIGHT ENERGY DIRECTLY TO CHEMICAL ENERGY

All of the plants that are used in flower- and plant-producing greenhouses are green plants—they contain chlorophyll and can manufacture food in the presence of light. The chemical energy that results from this conversion of light is the carbohydrates and proteins of which the plants and flowers are built. With close attention to the management of the greenhouse environment, the proper kind and amount of chemical energy is produced, resulting in a good quantity of high-quality flowers and plants.

Greenhouses are used so that the light energy of the sun will be available to the plants daily, while temperatures and moisture are controlled as required. Glass transmits all light rays from the sun except the ultraviolet and infrared. The loss of the ultraviolet is not of consequence because there is no evidence of beneficial effects from it on plants. The light energy that is absorbed by the plants, soil, and equipment changes to heat energy with evolution of infrared rays which cannot pass back through the glass. This causes an accumulation of heat in the greenhouse that eventually needs to be dissipated by convection currents through the ventilators, or mechanically by use of exhaust fans.

Although the primary interest in light in the greenhouse is in the portion of the light that becomes directly changed to chemical energy in the process of photosynthesis in the plant, it is only a small portion of the total light energy that is utilized in this way. Most of the sunlight does convert to heat energy as it contacts the air and objects on earth, and because of this the heat effects must be considered at the same time as the light effects.

- **THERE IS A TREMENDOUS AMOUNT OF ENERGY THAT REACHES THE EARTH FROM THE SUN**

The side of the earth towards the sun receives the light energy commonly called daylight, and the opposite side of the earth is shaded from the sun's light rays, or in the dark. Because the earth rotates on its axis once every 24 hours, most areas of the earth receive some light energy (day) each rotation and a period without any (night). The length of the day and night periods depends on the location on the earth and the time of the year. At the equator the days and nights are approximately 12 hours each the year-round. For other locations on the earth equal-length days and nights occur only at the spring equinox in March and the fall equinox in September. The length of day varies with the location in latitude on the earth. At the North Pole the day length is from 24 hours in late June to 0 hours in late December. At 40° North latitude the days are about 16 hours long in late June to about 9 hours long in late December. In addition to the days' being of shorter duration in the northern hemisphere from September to March, the light intensity is less also because of the angle at which the sunlight reaches the earth at that time of the year.

The difference between day and night seems like a rather elementary sort of thing, but it is not quite that simple. For some purposes, it might be satisfactory to consider sunrise as being the start of day and sunset the end, and for others it might be more appropriate to determine day length by the sensitivity of the light sensor. For photoperiodic response in plants, the day starts and ends at about one foot-candle—the plant will recognize daylight actually before sunrise and for some time after sunset. The photosynthetic day length for plants is much shorter because a few hundred or more foot-candles of light are required for photosynthesis to take place.

The comments here are based on a location about 40° North latitude—Columbus, Ohio. Although all locations at 40° North latitude will have roughly the same day length, light intensity may vary considerably, depending on elevation and cloud cover. At higher elevations the light has less air to pass through, resulting in higher light intensity at those locations. Some areas average less cloud cover than others, and for that reason the light intensity is higher there.

Light intensity is measured and expressed in various ways. The most common term to the flower grower is foot-candle, which is measured by a light meter (not a photographer's light meter). A greenhouse manager should have a light meter for sensing light intensity; however, if he does not have one he usually can borrow one for temporary use from the local electric power company. The maximum light intensity varies from more than 10,000 foot-candles during the summer to just a few thousand foot-candles during the winter; on some winter days the maximum light intensity is just a few hundred foot-candles. It must be kept in mind that during the winter, both the length of day and the light intensity are reduced, resulting in a severe drop in light energy reaching the plants in the greenhouse. Plants vary in the amount of light required for photosynthesis, but the light needed for plants usually grown in the greenhouse probably is from about 1,000 to 7,000 foot-candles, depending on the kind of plant.

The daily light intensity increases gradually from zero in the morning to the maximum in early afternoon and then gradually decreases to zero again in the evening. A day in which the noon light intensity is optimum for photosynthesis has something less than adequate light intensity the rest of the day.

The foot-candle means of expressing light quantity is a momentary measurement. Another means of sensing light quantity is with an instrument that records the heat which results from the conversion of the light energy that reaches a unit in the instrument, and the value is expressed as calories per square centimeter per minute. It is possible to use such a value in making energy calculations. For a reference point between the two methods of measurement, light intensity of 6,700 foot-candles for one minute equals about one calorie per cm^2 per minute. The daily total light energy at Columbus, Ohio, varies from about 500 calories per cm^2 in summer to about 50 calories per cm^2 in mid-winter. There is more than enough light at any location in the United States during the summer, but during the winter, light quantity is very critical. It is at that time of year that the geographical location of the greenhouse is of great importance. In December it could be expected that Chicago, Illinois, would have a daily total light quantity of 50 calories per cm^2, Boston, Massachusetts, 100 calories per cm^2, Davis, California, 150 calories per cm^2, and Boulder, Colorado, 200 calories per cm^2.

The heat term that is familiar to greenhouse operators is *British thermal unit.* Expressing the sunlight energy values in terms of BTU might be more meaningful. A greenhouse of 6,000 square feet would require about 900,000 BTU heat per hour to maintain 60°F. temperature at minus 10°F. outdoors. At midday during the summer it would not be unusual for the light energy of the sun to develop 1,000,000 BTU per hour as it converts to heat energy after contact with the plants, soil, and equipment in the greenhouse. In spite of dreary light conditions during the winter, 100,000 to 200,000 BTU per hour of heat energy could result from the light energy reaching the greenhouse at midday.

- **THE OPTIMUM QUANTITY OF LIGHT SHOULD BE APPLIED AND THE REQUIRED TEMPERATURE RANGE MAINTAINED FOR THE PLANTS BEING GROWN**

This is a very specific relationship. The light intensity requirement for gloxinia is lower and the temperature needed is higher than for chrysanthemum. Some crops have the same light and temperature requirements and may be grown in the same area, but those that do differ must be grown separately for good results.

Greenhouses are designed to admit the maximum amount of light. In spite of this there is not enough light intensity available during the winter, and the daily duration of light is not long enough. In the summer the light at midday is too intense, but the daily duration of light is suitable for photosynthesis. The greenhouse must be managed so that all possible light is transmitted into the greenhouse in the winter and the light partially excluded during the summer. A thorough job must be done in the fall of cleaning the glass and removing overhead obstacles in the greenhouse. The glass cleaning must be coordinated with the expected weather conditions for the area. It will help to keep records of when glass was cleaned in the past and resulting conditions. Unfortunately weather conditions are variable from year to year, and in spite of good intentions the glass will be cleaned either too early or too late on occasion. If the light intensity is greater than desired in early fall the solution is to erect tobacco cloth temporarily above the crops. In fact the best plan is to have some tobacco cloth on hand for this use as needed in the fall. If the dark weather is premature in the fall and comes before the glass cleaning job is completed, the only solution is to clean the glass as soon as possible when the weather permits.

Whatever method that is used for reducing the light intensity in the greenhouse in the summer, it must be effective for reducing the light, but it must be rather easily removed as needed. The most effective shade would be a system which could be applied and removed with a minimum of time, labor, and expense. The primary benefit with an easily installed shade system occurs at either end of the shading season. Typical examples at Columbus, Ohio, are very bright and hot weather for several days in April or early May, followed by dark and cool weather for several days or a few weeks. In the fall a few dark days in September may be followed by bright weather in October again before the dull days of winter set in. The weather patterns may vary considerably within short distances. Cleveland weather is quite different from Columbus weather, and further differences can be expected in Cincinnati, illustrating that it is necessary to be acquainted with local weather patterns and to react accordingly.

Most greenhouse operators choose to reduce the light intensity in the greenhouse by spraying shading compound on the exterior of the glass. Apparently they believe or have determined that this method is the most effective and/or economical. This may be true, but it does have a permanence that can be a problem, particularly at either end of the season. The alternative is to erect cloth or plastic screen shade above the plants. The fabrics used most commonly are either light muslin or tobacco cloth. They must be installed in such a way that they do not impede air movement in the greenhouse. If they can be applied so that they can be adjusted daily as needed, that would be a definite advantage, particularly in spring and fall.

• LIGHT FROM ELECTRIC POWER CAN BE USED TO SUPPORT PHOTOSYNTHESIS IN SOME SPECIAL SITUATIONS

Light from electric power can be used as the sole source of light to grow some plants for the entire period of the crop. Excellent quality gloxinias or Saint Paulias can be grown in this way because the light requirement for photosynthesis in those plants is rather low—600 foot-candles, 16 hours per day. This produces growth of the plants comparable to that of plants grown under sunlight in the greenhouse when the maximum light for the day is 1,000 foot-candles. Of course the plants under lights received the full 600 foot-candles of light for the entire 16-hour days, whereas the greenhouse plants had the naturally graduated light intensity from zero to 1,000 foot-candles and back to zero daily. A few commercial units have been established for growing these plants solely under lights, but apparently this method has been found to be less economical than growing plants in greenhouses in sunlight.

Some growth chambers are designed for supplying optimum air environment conditions for plants. These chambers may provide light intensities of 2,500 foot-candles or more, and temperature and air movement are controlled. It does not appear that such units will have commercial application because the cost of installation and the operating costs are high. The cost of such units is in the vicinity of $200 per square foot. They can be fine research tools.

There has been interest through the years in the use of supplemental light in the greenhouse to promote photosynthesis, and it has been considered impractical or uneconomical. There just has not seemed to be a good way to provide several thousand foot-candles of light from electric power. Advances in equipment and increased understanding of the various effects of light on plants suggest that some type of electric lighting may be developed which could be used commercially to promote photosynthesis and growth of plants. This may involve high intensity lamps, or it may be possible that low intensity lamps of certain specific colors, or lighting at specific times of the day or in certain rotations, will have commercial adaptations. The greenhouse manager should keep an open mind on this subject.

- **THE EFFECT OF DAY LENGTH OR NIGHT LENGTH ON PLANTS**
  IS OF GREAT COMMERCIAL IMPORTANCE

The initial work with photoperiod and plant growth and development referred to day length and that term continues in popular usage even though it has been demonstrated that it is length of night that produces the effect. On the surface this apparent play with words may seem to be quibbling, but in fact commercial use is made of the fact by lighting in the middle of the night to produce short nights rather than lighting at dusk to produce long days.

For the photoperiodic effect, the plants react to very low light intensity—some plants as low as 1 foot-candle. Plants of the same species may vary in the amount of light required for the photoperiodic effect. As little as 2 or 3 foot-candles is sufficient for some varieties of chrysanthemums, and others require twice that quantity of light. In general, poinsettias are more sensitive to light for the day-length effect than chrysanthemums.

Plants react to day length in many different ways, but the best known effect is on flowering; and the most usual concept here is that some plants will flower in long days and others in short days—an either/ or sort of relationship in which they are known as absolute or qualitative day-length plants.

The chrysanthemum is an outstanding commercial example of this day-length effect. It increases in stem length and produces leaves in long-days, but in short days growth terminates with the formation of flowers. It is an absolute or qualitative short-day plant. Actually chrysanthemums can form flower buds in long-days, but those buds do not continue to develop into flowers. If long-days continue, shoots develop in the axils of the leaves below the flower bud, and these shoots subsequently by-pass it. The plants that flower regardless of day length, and whose time of flowering cannot be hastened by either long-days or short-days, are known as day-neutral plants. Some plants, although they will flower in either short or long-days, will flower more rapidly if they are given the more suitable day length. These are known as quantitative or facultative day-length plants. Snapdragons, carnations, and roses will flower more rapidly during naturally short-days if they are given short-nights by lighting mid-way in the dark period. These are examples of quantitative or facultative long-day plants. In commercial practice there is no question about the use of artificially short-days to promote flowering in chrysanthemums or poinsettias. They are qualitative short-day plants, and unless short-day treatment is given during naturally long days there will be no crop. The decision to light the quantitative long-day plants such as roses, snapdragons, or carnations in naturally short days is based on whether the reduced length of crop time will compensate for the cost of electrical installation and power.

The quantity of light and the length of the light period (or dark period) required for the photoperiodic effect vary somewhat with the plants involved. For most commercial flower crops, 10 foot-candles is a safe minimum quantity of light; however, the Easter lily apparently requires about a 15-foot-candle minimum. In providing artificially long-days for chrysanthemums or poinsettias the 10-foot-candle minimum is used, and the best method is to provide the electric lighting in the middle of the night to assure a short night, rather than extend the day-length by lighting at either dawn or dusk. For the long-day photoperiodic effect the daily length of light must be in excess of 14½ hours, and for practical purposes a 15-hour day is used. The short-night then would be 9 hours or less each 24-hour period. To provide long days during the time of the year when the days are short, electric light should be used over the plants for a period of time each night around midnight. The lights must be on long enough so that neither portion of the night is nine hours long. The length of the daily lighting period will have to be determined by the time of the year and the latitude of the location. In most commercial situations it is considered wise to provide more than the minimum length of light, and because of this, at 40° N. latitude two-hour lighting is used daily around midnight in June and July; three-hour lighting for August and September, and again in April and May; and four-hour lighting for the months from October through March. At the equator three-hour lighting should probably be used the year-round, to assure long days. If long days were to be provided for chrysanthemum plants at the North Pole, the daily lighting period would have to be increased gradually from 3 hours in October to 15 hours in December and then could be gradually decreased to 3 hours again in April. This is strictly hypothetical, because there would not be sufficient light energy at the North Pole during the winter to support photosynthesis, and the plants probably would die.

The photoperiodic mechanism in plants apparently senses the red end of the spectrum more readily than other qualities of light, and because of this the incandescent light is the best choice of equipment, as the light emission from it is favorable in red. There are several ways in which electric lights may be installed over plants. One of the most common and practical systems is to install incandescent lights with reflectors every 4 feet, the length of the bench. If 60-watt lamps are used, they should be positioned about 2 feet above the tops of the plants, and that should provide a minimum of 10 foot-candles of light for the plants in a 4-foot-wide bench. Provision needs to be made so that the lights may be raised as the plants grow. For chrysanthemums the lights would need to be from about 2 feet above the soil at planting time to about 3 feet above the soil at the end of the lighting period, because the mum plants should be about one foot high at the start of short days. If it is desired to install the lights at a fixed height, it is probably best to hang them from the crossbar for the black cloth support. This will place the lights at about 4 feet above the soil and will require that lamps of 75 watts or greater be used to provide the light necessary for the small plants when they are first benched.

It has been demonstrated that the light interruption of the night does not need to be a period of continuous light—it can be flashing or intermittent light. Various time intervals may be used, but the one which has received most commercial acceptance is a minimum of 20 foot-candles of light each night, during a four-hour period from 10 p.m. to 2 a.m. with the lights on for 6 minutes and off for 24 minutes. With such an arrangement it is most economical to light five areas during the same four-hour period, using the same control equipment. Because only one-fifth of the lights are on at any one time, the power demand is only about one-fifth, and smaller service wire can be used for the installation. The familiar term for this intermittent lighting is cyclic lighting. It can produce the same results in plants as continuous lighting can for the entire period, but it must be understood that this lighting is close to the threshold, and conditions must be carried out exactly. Cyclic lighting does require more equipment—controllers, clocks, relays, and switches—, but the smaller-diameter service wire and reduction in power may offset this.

The long-day lighting system can be completely mechanized so that the lighting will be controlled by electric power as needed, but a check system should be used to verify that the lighting is being done satisfactorily. If a night man is employed, he should verify that the areas to be lighted are in fact lighted each night. He should also check to see if every lamp is operating and replace those that are defective. If a night man is not employed, a clock may be placed in each circuit that is to be used and the following morning the clocks checked to verify how long each area was lighted. A check program should be established to detect defective lamps, and possibly the best routine is to have an individual turn on the lights once a week during the day and make visual inspection.

A light meter should be used periodically to determine that the minimum light intensity is being supplied to the entire area. Because of the use of too small wire in the circuit or added power consumption, a voltage drop may occur, with a resulting reduction in light intensity.

If the design of the lighting system is such that the lights need to be raised as the plants grow, failure to raise the lights causes the plants farthest from the lights to grow above the lighted area. The newly expanded leaves are the most receptive to light, and if they are above the light the plant will react as though it is in short-days, in spite of the lower portion of the plant being in long-days.

Care must be taken so that light from the lighted areas does not reach plants that should be in short-days. If there is any question about conflict with the light, drop cloths should be used—or in some instances it is more efficient to pull black cloth over either the lighted area or the short-day area. Sometimes plants must be shielded from extraneous light. The day-length effect for poinsettias requires very little light energy. Street or alley lights or lighting from commercial establishments next door, such as service stations or shopping centers, may be sufficient to have long-day effect on them. Poinsettias are so sensitive to light that the plants in the vicinity of the night light over the thermometer may remain in vegetative growth because of the few minutes the night man has it on each night while he checks the temperature.

During naturally long-days if short-days are required for the correct photoperiod response of the plants, light is excluded from the plants for a portion of the day. Commercially this is done by drawing black cloth or black plastic on a framework over the plants. The plants must be totally enclosed so that the light intensity available to the plants is less than 1 foot-candle. For the plants commonly grown in the greenhouse, the critical length of short-day is about 13½ hours, but to make sure, a 12-hour day is usually used for the short-day effect during naturally long days. A shorter day than 12 hours may be used, but this may present other problems. Placing black cloth over plants too early in the day removes light that would be used for photo-synthesis, resulting in reduced food supply in the plants; and it causes unduly high temperatures for the plants, which increases the rate of respiration, further depleting the food supply.

It must be understood and appreciated that the act of drawing black cloth over plants to produce short-days will in fact only ac-complish this if the light is limited below the amount that the plants recognize as daylight. Black cloth or plastic excludes a percentage of the light, but not all. It is during the high-light-intensity portion of the year—spring to fall—that black cloth shading is done, and there is no cloth dense enough to produce short-days during midday. It can only be expected that the black cloth will effectively limit the light at dusk and dawn. On this basis it is reasonable that the black cloth be applied at 7 p.m. and removed at 7 a.m.—or if daylight time is being observed rather than standard time, it would be better to use 8 p.m. and 8 a.m. If there is no extraneous light in the area, there is no advantage in having the black cloth over the plants from about 10 p.m. to 4 a.m. (time adjustment needs to be made for daylight or standard time, time of the year, and the latitude of location), and if it could be ar-ranged there may be an advantage (better air movement and cooler temperatures) in removing the black cloth for that period of the night.

Many greenhouse operators prefer to have the black cloth pulled over the plants before the work crew leaves at 5 p.m. and have it removed at 8 a.m. when the crew reports for work. It fits in better with the work schedule to handle the black cloth in that way, but it does not provide the best conditions for the plants. In the three hours additional time that the cloth is over the plants that time is lost for food manufacturing and the temperature around the plants becomes too warm. On daylight time the problem is worse because the black cloth will then be pulled over the plants at 4 p.m. sun time. In many greenhouses black-cloth pulling has been mechanized so that the entire shading operation is done with electric power. It then becomes a simple operation to have the shade pulled at the best time for the plants. If it is not possible to mechanize this operation, a shade-pulling crew should be brought in each evening to handle the job.

Some growers like to conserve energy by not pulling the black cloth each night over chrysanthemums. It is possible to skip shading once a week—such as every Sunday—without bad results other than some slowdown in time of flowering. Skipping the shading more often than that causes uneven flowering as well as delay in flowering.

There are some exceptions, but once shading is started it should be continued daily until the flower buds are showing color.

There has been considerable interest through the years in an easier and more economical method of giving plants long-day or short-day treatment other than lighting them and pulling black cloth. Looking back less than 200 years, the relationship between plants and light was not understood at all. Then in late 1700 or early in 1800 the concept began developing that plants used light in the manufacture of food, and in 1864 it was demonstrated that starch developed in the chloroplasts during the process. In following years it was learned that plants vary in the amount of light required for photosynthesis to proceed at full capacity, but rather high-intensity light is needed, ranging from around 1,000 foot-candles upward to 6,000 foot-candles. Subsequently it was found that it is primarily the blue light (around 450 nm) and red light (around 670 nm) which is absorbed by the green pigment, chlorophyll, and utilized in photosynthesis. There really was no reason to expect more from light than this wonderful arrangement for making food, but in early 1900 it was learned that there is a day-length effect on some plants. The initial finding was that some plants flowered in short-days but not in long-days. It took awhile for the commercial aspects of this finding to be considered. Before this time chrysanthemums had only been flowered in the fall of the year, and it was accepted that this was the nature of these plants, so be it. However, by late 1930 and early 1940 it had been demonstrated that flowering in chrysanthemums could be manipulated by providing short-days with black cloth and long-days with electric lights; and in the ensuing years a great commercial revolution took place, spawning a new industry that produces chrysanthemum flowers every day the year-round. Eventually it was learned that a very small quantity of light energy is required for the day-length effect—in the order of 1 to 10 foot-candles—, and about 1950 it was discovered that it is a blue pigment in the plant which absorbs the light and triggers the day-length effects. It was named phytochrome, and it senses either red light (around 660 nm) or far-red light (around 730 nm). About 1960 yet another reactive system was reported for plants. It requires much less light energy than is needed for photosynthesis, but considerably more than is needed for the day-length effect—roughly 100 times more. Because of this greater light requirement, the name HER (high energy reaction) has been given this system. It is responsive to blue light (around 450 nm) and far-red light (around 730 nm). There is evidence of definite relationships between the phytochrome and HER systems in plants in which the HER system, in response to either blue or far-red light, may establish conditions which produce plant reactions following activation of the phytochrome system by either red light or far-red light. The response of plants to light can vary, depending on preceding conditions, and it is not possible to predict what future basic findings may have on commercial operations.

The reaction of plants to light is determined to varying degrees by temperature. This will be discussed in the section on temperature. In considering the response of plants to light, here it is assumed that a suitable temperature exists. It does need to be mentioned here, however, that in some instances promotion of flowering by low-temperature treatment (vernalization) may be replaced by day-length treatment. To some extent this is used commercially with Easter lilies by supplying long-days as soon as the shoot emerges through the soil. This suggests that there may be other possibilities in the use of either temperature or light treatments or combinations of temperature and light treatments to promote certain responses in plants. Apparently in these instances, in which similar plant response is obtained with either temperature control or light control, the same chemistry proceedings must have been set in motion in the plants.

It has been demonstrated in some long-day plants that treating them with gibberellic acid can produce the same effect as the vernalizing procedure with low temperature. This has been used to some extent with azaleas. Presumably the gibberellic acid treatment supplies one of the products of chemistry which would be formed in these long-day plants had they received the low-temperature, vernalization treatment.

The basic facts pertaining to plants and light are really of fairly recent origin—and knowledge and concepts in this field have been accelerating. The greenhouse operators' use and control of light are bound to change as new information and understanding develop, and it appears that this might include the use of different light qualities; different light regimes involving light quality, light intensity, or duration of light; supplanting or replacing light treatments with temperature manipulation; or supplying plants with one or more of the end products that would have been formed by the plant if a light treatment had been furnished. Some of these could lead to interesting commercial developments.

● CAREFUL CONTROL OF TEMPERATURE IS REQUIRED
  FOR DESIRED PLANT RESPONSE

The greenhouse operator soon learns that the temperature requirements for plants are quite specific. Temperatures are usually sensed with thermometers, and in the United States they are calibrated to the Fahrenheit scale, in which 32° is the freezing point and 212° is the boiling point of water. In some other parts of the world and commonly in research work the thermometer with Centigrade scale is used in which 0° is the freezing point and 100° is the boiling point of water. Some quick reference points between the two scales are: The so-called healthful room temperature for human beings, 68°F., is 20°C.; 59°F. is the same as 15°C., 50°F. equals 10°C., and 41°F. is the same temperature as 5°C. The relationship between the two scales becomes apparent in scanning this series—five units on the Centigrade scale equals nine units in the Fahrenheit scale.

Before thermometers are installed they should be checked for accuracy, and possibly the easiest way to do this is to insert the thermometer bulbs into a bucket containing ice cubes and a small quantity of water. If the Fahrenheit thermometers do not register 32° or the Centigrade thermometers 0° in such a situation, they should be discarded.

Some thermometers are used in the greenhouse for determining soil temperatures, but the most common use for thermometers is sensing air temperatures. Really the information that is needed is the plant temperature, but there are some difficulties is sensing plant temperatures directly. The next best possibility is to assume that the air surrounding the plant is a fair indicator of the temperature of the plant. It is important to acknowledge that the thermometer is being used to evaluate the plant temperature. It is not just a means of determining the temperature of the air in the greenhouse. Considered on this basis, it is understandable that the thermometer must be placed as close as possible to the plant. A thermometer installed at eye level in the greenhouse may be a fine convenience for the grower checking temperatures, but it can be expected to indicate the temperature for plants only in the vicinity and at that level. Plants at ground level in this house would usually be in cooler air than the thermometer at about a 5-foot height, and plants on shelves above the thermometer would be in warmer air. For an accurate assessment of plant temperature, the thermometers must be placed where the plants are. Unless effective air-circulation fans are used in the greenhouse, it should be expected that there will be a several-degree difference in temperature from the coolest temperature at the base to the warmest near the ridge.

It is unusual in a greenhouse if the temperatures are uniform from side to side or end to end. Sometimes this horizontal temperature gradient can be minimized by changes in the heating or air-movement systems, but the grower won't even know the gradient exists unless a sufficient number of thermometers are placed in the house so that temperatures for various locations may be compared. The most common procedure is to place the thermometer at eye level in the vicinity of the machine from which the ventilators are operated. If it is felt necessary to maintain the thermometer at that location in the house, then the manager must make enough temperature readings around the house so that he will know what temperature reading at that thermometer will provide the correct temperature where the plants are. The same procedure must be followed in situations where temperatures are sensed by thermostat, and heat or ventilation is controlled electrically. If the thermostat is not in the immediate vicinity of the plants, it will not provide the correct temperature for the plants unless some human being determines the temperature differential between the two locations and then makes the proper setting on the thermostat.

Several types of thermometers are available. For sensing air temperatures, a wall thermometer is used commonly, mounted on wood, and oriented to face north so that it will not be in the direct rays of the sun. For highly accurate air-temperature sensing, the thermometer is placed in an insulated and aspirated box to make sure that the sun's rays do not affect it directly, but that a representative sample of air is in the immediate vicinity of the bulb at all times. This type of thermometer gives a momentary indication of the temperature. Sometimes it would be helpful to have a record of what the air temperature has been in an area for the past period. Recording thermometers can be used for this purpose. They usually have a chart on a drum which makes one revolution a week. Periodic inspection of the chart will indicate the kind of corrective action that needs to be taken to provide the right temperature regime for the plants. In some instances it helps to know the high temperature and the low temperature experienced in an area during the period, and for this purpose a minimum-maximum thermometer may be used. These thermometers are of limited value, however, as they indicate only the extremes, without any reference to the duration of that temperature. For most purposes a recording thermometer is a more satisfactory temperature indicator than a minimum-maximum thermometer.

Soil thermometers are indispensable for use in determining temperatures in propagation beds and in soil being steamed. The temperature is critical for both operations. It is possible to use dairy-type thermometers to monitor soil temperatures, or instruments made specifically for this purpose may be used. They have a stem or probe that can be inserted into the soil, and they must be placed at the right location and depth to assure a meaningful reading.

If a practical means of determining plant temperatures directly could be used, temperature probably could be controlled more accurately, because air temperatures usually lag behind plant temperatures. Thermocouples may be placed in plants but this does not appear to be practical for commercial use. It is possible, however, that infrared thermometers may be used eventually in greenhouses for some evaluation of plant temperatures.

- ● A WIDE RANGE OF TEMPERATURE IS REQUIRED TO PRODUCE FLOWERS AND PLANTS IN THE GREENHOUSE

For the various activities involved in the production of flowers and plants, a wide range of temperature is needed. Flowering is promoted in some plants if they are subjected to cool temperatures for a certain period of time before being placed in the greenhouse for forcing in warm temperatures. Promotion of flowering by use of cool temperatures is known as vernalization. The effective temperatures for vernalization are from about 45° to 35°F.—although temperatures just above freezing are used in some instances. The plant must be at a certain stage of development at the time it is placed in the vernalizing temperature, and a uniformly cool temperature must be supplied for at least a minimum period of time. Advantage may be taken of naturally cool outdoor temperatures from fall to spring by placing the plants outdoors, with enough protection to keep them from freezing; bulbs may be flatted or potted and covered with enough straw, sawdust, or soil to prevent them from freezing. Plants such as azaleas or hydrangeas may be given their vernalizing treatment in cold frames, temporary plastic houses, or greenhouses operated for that purpose. There usually is no need to monitor temperatures for the bulbs because the covering is sufficient to take care of great temperature variation. For plants in cold frames or common storage facilities, enough thermometers must be used so that additional cover may be applied as needed to prevent freezing. If refrigerators or cold-storage units are used for vernalizing, thermometers must be placed among the plants being cooled so that it can be observed if the proper temperatures are are being maintained.

At the other end of the scale are the temperatures used for steaming soil and equipment. The primary reasons for using steam are the elimination of plant-disease pathogens, plant pests, and weeds, and this requires a uniform temperature in the range of 160°F. to 180°.

Plant propagation proceeds more rapidly at warm temperatures, and it is a very narrow temperature range that is effective for each kind of plant. There can be no compromise on control of temperature in the propagation area—there must be acurate temperature-sensing and heat-control facilities in the propagation bench. The propagation area needs to be operated separately from the general growing area of the green-house, so that the warmer temperatures can be maintained.

It may not be a necessity, but there is a definite advantage in hav-ing a refrigerated area for use with most greenhouse crops. For general use it would be operated at 45°F., but for specific purposes it might be run cooler but usually not below 35°F. The primary use for this facility would be for short-term cool storage of cut flowers or pot plants before marketing. It also could be used for holding rooted cuttings between the time they are received and the time they are planted.

All of the foregoing discussion refers to temperatures maintained uniformly day or night—these are temperature requirements regard-less of time of day. For plants growing in the greenhouse the best re-sults come from the use of one temperature regime for the night and another for the day. Usually the daytime temperature should be 5° to 10°F. warmer than the nighttime temperature, depending on whether the day is overcast or sunny. Each kind of plant responds best to a rather narrow temperature range. It is not a matter of simply hav-ing the area above or below a certain temperature; the temperature should be within two degrees of the most favorable temperature. If that temperature is 52°F. for carnations, it should be maintained from 51° to 53°F. during the night, and 56° to 58°F. on an overcast day, and 61° to 63°F. on a sunny day. Each kind of plant has its own narrow temperature range, and for most of the plants grown in the green-house the night temperature is someplace between 50° and 65°F., although there are a few kinds of plants that have their best growth at 70°F. With some crops it is advisable to vary the temperature with the stage of development of the crop—possibly using a higher tempera-ture in the early stages of growth, with cooler temperatures toward the finish. In spite of this, the temperature range must be narrow at each stage.

• THE SUN IS A SOURCE OF HEAT IN THE GREENHOUSE

Greenhouses are constructed to admit the maximum amount of light, so that the plants will have a sufficient amount of light energy for the manufacture of food in the process of photosynthesis. Incidentally, a considerable portion of this light changes from light to heat energy when it contacts the plants, soil, and equipment in the greenhouse. About one-half the total energy of the sun that reaches the earth's surface is infrared radiation from 760 nm to 2,300 nm, which is radiation that cannot be distinguished by the eye. In spite of the eye's not seeing the infrared radiation, the body does sense it because of the heat developed when these rays are absorbed. Plants also will be warmed by the infrared portion of the sun radiation; however, because glass does not transmit infrared rays, plants outdoors will be affected more than those under glass.

It is, then, essentially only the visible portion of the sun's energy which is transmitted into the greenhouse and becomes a source of heat. A large share of the light energy that is absorbed by the plants and surroundings in the greenhouse changes to heat energy. These heated objects then radiate a portion of this heat to the atmosphere as infrared rays. Some of these infrared rays are absorbed by the air or other objects, some are transmitted, and some are reflected. Those that reach the glass are reflected or absorbed, causing a continuous build-up of heat in the greenhouse during sunny days.

A substance is heated directly by the sun only if radiant energy is absorbed. The amount of sun's energy absorbed will depend on the amount that is available to the substance, plus the receptivity. Dark-colored objects absorb more light energy than light-colored ones and thus become hotter. The greatest light absorption is by black objects. We see them as black because no light rays are reflected back—they are all absorbed, giving the greatest potential for development of heat in that object. White objects are the opposite. All light rays are reflected, and thus the potential for development of heat is low. For objects in the same sunlight, black soil will be hotter than light-colored soil, white flowers will be cooler than red flowers, and yellow-green plants will absorb less light than dark-green plants.

Air is quite transparent to light. Light is transmitted directly through air, and because it is not absorbed the potential for heating the air directly by light is low. Plants, soil, and other objects in the greenhouse become heated readily in sunlight and in turn become radiators in transmitting heat to the air. Heat is transferred from plants by radiation (as just discussed), conduction (primarily from leaf to air in direct contact with it), and convection (a flow of warmer air rising from the vicinity of the leaf to the atmosphere in the greenhouse).

The sun is a marvelous source of heat for plants during the heating season in the greenhouse, but some problems can be encountered if the mode of heating is not understood. When the sun appears, the plant temperature will rise faster than the air temperature, because the relatively dark-colored plants absorb much more light than the air. When the sun disappears, the plant temperature drops faster than the air temperature, as the plant continues to lose heat at a fast rate to the air and surroundings. During clear weather the temperature differential between air and plant can be reduced by introducing heat by means of the heating system into the greenhouse before sunup and before sundown. By introducing more heat into the greenhouse before sunup the transition from night temperatures to day temperatures (about a 10°F. rise) will not be so abrupt as it would be if it were handled solely by the heat generated from the sun. Starting to introduce more heat from the heating system before sundown should maintain uniformity between plant and air temperature as the sun disappears. The daytime temperature should be maintained by means of the heating system until the sun is down, and then generally reduced to the night temperature.

When the days are continually overcast during cold weather, there is not sufficient heat gained from the sun to maintain temperatures in the greenhouse, and plant and air temperatures are maintained uniformly with the heating system day and night.

Maintaining uniform plant and air temperatures is something of a nightmare when outdoor temperatures are cold and the sky is alternately clear and then overcast. Neither automated nor manual methods are quite capable of anticipating the temperature changes caused by the appearance and disappearance of the sun. Most satisfactory results will probably result from maintaining uniform heat from the heating system and venting excess heat when the sun appears.

The sun is a considerable comfort as a source of heat during the winter—in fact, if it could be arranged, most growers would like it if the sun could be tapped for heat both day and night for that season of the year. During the summer we enjoy the amount of light that we get from the sun, and the plants thrive in it; but the accompanying heat can work a hardship. Heat reduction for greenhouse plants is attempted in two different manners—reduction of the amount of sunlight by providing partial shade over the plants or by the removal of some of the excess heat from the greenhouse. This is probably an appropriate place to make mention that temperature is regulated by the addition or removal of heat. It may be true that something becomes cold or colder, but it is important to realize that it became cold not because cold was added but because heat was withdrawn. Cold exists only because of the lack of heat, in much the same sense as a vacuum is an absence of matter or that black is not a color but a lack of color. It was noted earlier that plants produce the best growth within narrow temperature ranges. This is true summer or winter, and it is the same temperature range that is effective in both seasons. Although plants may be grown successfully during the summer at somewhat higher temperatures than during the winter, most crops will benefit from some reduction of the normal temperature that season of the year. It is best to use the two-pronged attack of reduction of the amount of light entering the greenhouse plus the removal of some of the heat that is generated. Reduction of the amount of light may be handled by either the use of shading compound on the glass or cloth placed above the plants—or a combination of the two. Shade on the glass should be somewhat more effective because it actually prevents a portion of the sunlight from entering the structure. Cloths used inside the glass keep a portion of the light from direct contact with the plants but would not actually keep the heat out of the greenhouse. Some different methods possibly could be used for removing heat from the greenhouse, but the most practical method uses the mechanical movement of air with exhaust fans and the introduction of air from the exterior through moistened pads. On the trip through the pads, heat from the air is used to evaporate some of the water—thus cooling the entering air. For each gallon of water evaporated, about 8,800 BTU of heat would be removed from the incoming air. The rate of evaporation of water from the pad depends on the temperature of the incoming air and the amount of moisture in the air. Because of the usual dry air in Arizona and moist air in Florida, it could be expected that fan and pad cooling would be more efficient in Arizona than in Florida. For an estimate of the amount of cooling that could be expected from fan and pad cooling in your area, use a sling psychrometer; the difference in temperature on the dry bulb and wet bulb would be the maximum potential cooling. By the way, the sling psychrometer should be part of the greenhouse operator's equipment. It is the best device for determining the amount of moisture in the air, and there are many situations in the greenhouse in which air moisture is critical. Unfortunately the name, sling psychrometer, sounds foreboding, as though it must be expensive and difficult to use, but it is not. It is very simple to use, and the same merchant who sells thermometers should be able to supply the sling psychrometer at probably something less than $20.00.

Fan and pad cooling systems originated in southwestern United States. Summer temperatures were so high in that area that production of flowers and plants in the greenhouse without some method of reducing temperature was almost impossible. In other areas, where summer temperatures were not so high or air moisture was greater, flower and plant production could continue during the summer, and the use of fan and pad cooling was questioned. It is now realized that sufficient temperature reduction is possible in most areas of the country to cause enough improvement in plant growth to make the expenditure for fan and pad equipment economically worthwhile.

Actually it was the advent of fan and pad cooling that introduced mechanical movement of air in the greenhouse, and that has resulted in benefits beyond summertime use. In fact the use of exhaust fans for greenhouse ventilation any time of the year reduced the requirement for ridge ventilators and caused a small revolution in greenhouse design. If ridge ventilators are not needed for ventilation, it then is not necessary to have a ridge, and greenhouses may be designed as quonset or other type structures.

● SUPPLYING HEAT TO THE GREENHOUSE BY MEANS OTHER THAN
THE SUN REQUIRES A LOT OF ENGINEERING

The necessary heat must be generated, it must be transported and distributed to where it is needed, and it must be accurately controlled. Whenever possible, gas is used as fuel. The initial cost may be more per BTU heat developed, but handling and operating costs are so much lower with gas that the over-all costs are lower than either oil or coal. In many areas, because of the shortage of gas at some times of the year, it is necessary to have units that will use either gas or oil so that an instantaneous switch to oil can be made when the gas shortage develops.

In most greenhouse ranges it is practical to use a central heat-generating plant and distribute the heat from there to the various greenhouses. In some instances unit heaters are used in each greenhouse. These usually are gas-burner units with a motor-driven fan to force the heat away from the unit and establish convection currents for the distribution of heat throughout the greenhouse. It is difficult to install such units so that the heat is distributed uniformly horizontally and vertically in the greenhouse. The initial investment for this type of heating is low, and in some situations it could be a suitable means of supplying heat to the greenhouse. It is essential that unit heaters in greenhouses be supplied with a source of air from the exterior to prevent the accumulation of products of combustion. The size of air inlet and vent should be prescribed by the manufacturer of the unit heater. The controls for the unit-heater fan should provide for both manual and automatic operation so that it would be possible to have the fan in operation continuously when desired. In most instances it is best to have the fan in continuous operation, with the heater controlled by thermostat.

There have been some infrared unit-heater installations in greenhouses, but these have not gained in popularity because the initial cost is high, there is difficulty in providing uniform heating, and the considerable amount of overhead equipment limits the amount of sunlight available to the plants. Infrared heaters require venting and an air supply from the exterior in the same fashion as other unit heaters.

When unit heaters are used for heating the greenhouses, a boiler will have to be supplied solely to produce steam for steaming soil, or other means will have to be used for treating soil and equipment.

When heat for the greenhouse is generated at a central point, it must be in a form which is easily transported to and distributed throughout the greenhouses. Water seems to be the most convenient method for getting the heat to the greenhouse, and there are some advantages in using the gaseous form of water (steam) rather than the liquid form (hot water). When the fuel is ignited in the combustion chamber of the boiler, chemical energy is changed to heat energy, and this heat is transferred to the water in the boiler. If it is a steam boiler, the fire is regulated to continue to supply heat until a certain steam pressure is reached in the boiler. Many greenhouse boilers are operated at less than 15 pounds pressure, but some are designed to develop up to 90 pounds per square inch. The temperature of steam at 15 pounds per square inch is about 250°F., and at 90 pounds per square inch it is about 331°F. Steam may be transported to the greenhouse at the same pressure developed at the boiler or a lower pressure, but it is seldom distributed in the greenhouse at more than 5 pounds per square inch pressure or a temperature of about 227°F. The fire in the hot water boiler is controlled to provide water temperature from 145°F. to 180°F. as desired.

Both steam and hot water are closed systems in which the water is returned to the boiler after the heat has been distributed to the greenhouses. It is possible to distribute steam or hot water in the greenhouses and return the water to the boiler by having the boiler at the lowest level in the system, with heating lines pitched up to the farthest greenhouses and return lines pitched down towards the boiler. These gravity systems operate because of the weight difference per unit of steam or hot water and cold water. In some instances the entire heating system must be on about the same level, and then circulating pumps are used for hot water and return pumps for steam systems.

It is very desirable to build in some anticipation in the operation of the heating system. An accurate weather forecast is invaluable, and it has to be something more than "fair and warmer" or "possible showers." In most areas a realistic weather forecast may be obtained from operational personnel at military or commercial airports. It may require something more than routine arrangements to get these forecasts regularly, but it will be worth the effort. What is the weather going to be, and how fast is this change going to occur? With that information at hand, the required heat can be generated in the boiler room and the grower can adjust heating lines and ventilators in the greenhouse according to the anticipated change.

When heat is required in the greenhouse, the side lines (gutter or eave) should be the first ones activated. As more heat is required, either bench lines or overhead lines may be used as needed. This rotation should be used with either manual or mechanical operation of heating lines. When the heat requirement diminishes, the side lines should be the last ones to be turned off.

It is possible that the thermometers in the greenhouse may be located correctly for sensing temperature effects caused by the sun but not in the best position to indicate the effects from the heating lines. Enough thermometers must be placed in the greenhouse and observed during various heating regimes to determine the best placement of thermometers and the best rotation of heating lines.

There are many possible arrangements of heating lines in greenhouses which may require different methods of operation, but usually the minimum number of lines should be in operation, because this gives the most uniform heating throughout the greenhouse. Having too many lines in operation when a small amount of heat is required will cause rapid on and off operation of the lines, with too much heat supplied at the heat source end and not enough heat at the farther end.

There is not much of an argument over whether manual or mechanical control of heating is best. It just is not possible to hire the quality or quantity of personnel required to control heating. The best systems may use a blend of manual and mechanical control, in which the mechanical portion handles all the routine and the manual involves some thought and judgement. The system must be designed for the physical facilities and the personnel available, and most greenhouses will need a three-stage control, in which the side lines are activated first, followed by some of the bench or overhead lines, and finally with the operation of all lines. This could be handled manually or mechanically or by a combination of the two. Whatever the control system, it will be helpful if foresight can be built into it, so that weather and temperature trends are recognized and anticipatory action is taken, to avoid playing catch-up.

There will be different temperature trends from day to day and hour to hour, and it will be difficult to anticipate all of them correctly; but there are two routine trends which occur daily that should not be missed, and these are at dawn and dusk, when the source of heat changes. The heating system should be activated soon enough before dusk that the daytime temperature is maintained until dusk, followed by a gradual lowering to night temperature caused by a reduction in the amount of heat introduced into the greenhouse. This method of temperature control at dusk produces much more uniform temperatures than letting the night temperature establish naturally and then attempting to maintain it with the heating system. As mentioned earlier, heating before dusk will assure that the plant temperature will be maintained and will eliminate the possibility of moisture's forming on the plant surface. If some venting is done during dusk heating, there is the possibility of a reduction not only in the relative humidity of the greenhouse atmosphere, but also in moisture formation on the plant surface.

The controls should be adjusted at dawn so that the increase in temperature to day temperature is handled by the heating system, rather than the sun. Then as the sun takes over the heating job, the heating system can be phased out.

There is a direct relationship between heat and moisture quantity in the air, and it is generally stated in terms of warm air having a greater capacity to hold water vapor. This is a fair enough statement, but there are some benefits in thinking of it in terms of heat gain or loss. If the situation is such that heat is being transferred from the air (the temperature in the greenhouse is dropping), it can be expected that some of the water vapor in the air will change to the liquid form and settle out of the air. If heat is being added to the air (the temperature in the greenhouse is rising), it can be expected that the moisture in the air will remain in the gas form and additional moisture from surrounding objects may change from the liquid to gas state and thus increase the amount of water vapor in the air.

- ● REMOVING HEAT FROM THE GREENHOUSE DURING THE HEATING SEASON MAY
  BE DONE BY VENTING AND INTRODUCING COOL AIR FROM THE OUTDOORS

Traditionally, venting in greenhouses has been done by means of ventilators at the ridge, plus, in some instances, ventilators at the side walls. Such a ventilating system operates because hot air is lighter than cool air, causing convection currents in which the hot air rises and cool air descends. If the ventilators are open, the hot air continues to rise and exits from the greenhouse. It is replaced by cool air from the outdoors entering through the ventilators. The more air movement outdoors and the greater the temperature differential between indoors and out, the greater the exchange of air. When there is little air movement outdoors and the temperature is the same outdoors as in the greenhouse, there will be virtually no exchange of air. This situation seldom exists in the heating season, but it is rather common during the summer.

If the ventilators are handled manually, a good routine must be established for taking care of the job. Here is one of the jobs in which responsibility must definitely be assigned. Ventilation in the greenhouse cannot be done on the basis of let's everyone remember to do it. That invites inaction or overaction. The assigned individual must fully understand that he is responsible for maintaining the temperature in the greenhouse within one degree plus or minus of a given temperature by adjusting heating lines and/or ventilators. He should be supplied the information on weather trends for the next few hours so that he can take preparatory action. Usually the foreman should be the one to take care of heat and ventilation control. This will provide for the necessary control during the work day, but it leaves about two-thirds of each 24 hours plus week-ends and holidays to be handled by other individuals. This is the weak link in the production operations of many greenhouses. Temperature and ventilation control must be continuous, which would necessitate a night man's coming on duty at the time the day crew leaves plus a night man's continuing on duty until the day crew arrives in the morning each day. The foreman should have a good concept of the controls needed during the day, but the manager should expect that the night, week-end, and holiday control people will need special instructions, with sufficient checking to determine if they are following instructions. There is no good way to establish if instructions are understood other than by observing results.

Heating and ventilating must be coordinated; and usually if heat needs to be removed from the greenhouse, first the number of heating lines in operation are limited and then some ventilation is provided if further reduction in heat is required. If additional heat is needed in the greenhouse, the amount of ventilation should be reduced if possible, and then additional lines placed in operation if more heat is needed.

It must be recognized that greenhouses constructed of glass do provide for some exchange of air through the glass laps, and there is much more air movement through the glass in older greenhouses than in newly constructed ones. In extremely cold weather it may be possible to reduce the air flow through the glass (and incidentally the loss of heat) by introducing more moisture into the greenhouse air by spraying water on the heating lines and thus causing closure of the glass laps with frost. Because of the large size of the sheets, there are fewer laps in greenhouses covered with fiberglass, and less air exchange. Greenhouses covered with film plastic may have no laps at all and virtually no air exchange with the exterior through this covering.

Usually it is considered that ventilation is used only as a means of adjusting temperature in the greenhouse; however, it also is used in some instances to regulate the amount of moisture (relative humidity) in the greenhouse air and in other situations, to avoid possible deficiencies of oxygen or carbon dioxide in the greenhouse air by introducing air from the exterior.

Control of heating and ventilating may be mechanized, and many greenhouse operators have gone this route in recent years. Results have been generally good, although it is necessary to carefully evaluate if the mechanization is actually accomplishing what is needed.

In many greenhouses, control of heating was mechanized first, and ventilation later. It is relatively simple to design a system in which the temperature is sensed by thermostat, with the electrical impulse activating either an electric or pneumatic valve. With the boiler on electric controls, it is possible to activate it at a lower temperature, so that steam or hot water is available when it is needed in the greenhouse. It does take some doing to provide complete mechanization of controls of heating in the greenhouse, because of the need to supply the heat in stages. In many instances it will be economical and quite workable to adjust the second and third stage of heat quantity in the greenhouse manually.

When mechanization of ventilation was first considered in the greenhouse, it was natural to consider mechanization of existing ventilating equipment rather than the providing of an entirely new system, and this was handled by either electric motors or a pneumatic system. These could be installed for operation manually or by thermostat. On either basis, it saved time and personnel and often gave better temperature control in the greenhouse—particularly at times other than the regular working day.

At about the same time that mechanization of ventilation was being considered, fan and pad cooling was initiated in some parts of the country for better control of summer temperatures in the greenhouse. With fan and pad cooling, all of the air introduced into the greenhouse came through the pad, and the air exhausted went through the fan—the greenhouse ventilators remained closed. If the greenhouses were being ventilated throughout the summer without use of ventilators, it seemed possible that some system could be devised for use of the fans to provide ventilation without conventional ventilation equipment during the heating season. A portion of the fans could be used to exhaust air, but a different method of introducing air was needed. The method devised was the installation of a perforated poly tube the length of the greenhouse, toward the ridge, with one end closed and the other end attached to a shuttered inlet. With shutter open and some exhaust fans in operation, air entered the tube from outdoors and was distributed uniformly the length of the house.

The quantity of air that can be exchanged with this latter system is limited—suitable for ventilation practices during the winter, but certainly not sufficient for the summer. For summer ventilation and cooling it is necessary to change to the fan and pad system. For the variable weather periods spring and fall, there will be some days in which the fan and tube system is adequate, and others in which it is not. The design of the fan and pad system must provide for complete closure or opening of the pad area momentarily, so that spring and fall the greenhouse operator can elect to use either fan and tube or fan and pad systems, depending on the amount of ventilation required. For fan and pad ventilation, the exhaust fans must be capable of moving about 10 cubic feet of air per minute per square foot of greenhouse space. For ventilation during the heating season with fan and poly tube, the exhaust fans must be capable of moving air at the rate of 4 cubic feet per minute per square foot of greenhouse space. If the greenhouse is equipped for fan and pad ventilation, only about one-half the number of fans would need to be used for fan and poly tube ventilation.

● **MANY GREENHOUSES NEED CONTROLLED HIGHER TEMPERATURES FOR PROPAGATING PLANTS OR STARTING YOUNG PLANTS**

Propagation of plants proceeds faster at a temperature about 10°F. warmer than the temperature used during flower crop production. This temperature must be uniform and accurately controlled. The propagation area in most greenhouses is a very small portion of the total greenhouse area, and there often is reluctance to make the special provisions required to supply the necessary heat to that section. If management cannot be convinced that the boiler must be operated even if the propagation area is the only section of the greenhouse that needs heat, then other means of supplying heat for propagation must be used. Soil-heating cable using electric power and controlled by thermostat can provide the temperatures required in the propagation area, and they should be installed if there is any question about supplying heat with steam or hot water.

● **THE TWO PRIMARY USES FOR COOL TEMPERATURES WITH GREENHOUSE CROPS ARE FOR VERNALIZATION AND HOLDING**

Vernalization is the process in which plants or some plant parts are kept in cool temperatures for a few weeks so that flowering will be promoted when they are then placed in normally warm temperatures. The vernalizing temperature may vary somewhat with plant or other conditions, but it is generally considered to be below 50°F. The temperatures most commonly used are from 35° to 45°F. From fall to spring it is possible in some areas of the country to obtain these temperatures outdoors if some provision is made for protection of the plant from too cool temperatures and possibly from unseasonably high temperatures. With bulbs such as daffodils, tulips, and hyacinths, common procedure for years has been to pot or flat them in October and then place them on the ground outdoors and covered with about 6 inches of straw or wood shavings. Rooting occurs in the normally warm temperatures at the start, followed by vernalization in the naturally cool temperatures. Vernalization proceeds satisfactorily in such conditions, but there are some handling problems. If weather conditions are bad during the winter, it is difficult to dig and bring the bulbs in for forcing, as required.

Bulbs and plants may be vernalized in either common or refrigerated storage which may provide more accurate control over temperature and considerably improve handling conditions. For bulbs the storage must be maintained above 50°F. until rooting occurs, and then the temperature is dropped below 50°F. Plants such as azaleas and hydrangeas are placed directly in temperatures below 50°F. when they are placed in storage for vernalization. These plants also may be given their vernalizing treatment in cold frames or in greenhouses that are kept cool but above freezing.

Some bulbs may be given vernalization treatment before they are received by the greenhouse operator. Irises and Easter lilies commonly are handled this way, and they should be planted and placed in forcing temperatures immediately. Actually Easter lilies may be given their vernalization in other ways than just described. The grower may get the bulbs directly after they are dug and place them in 35°F. refrigerated storage for six weeks before potting them, or he may pot them as soon as they are received in October after digging and then give them vernalizing temperatures either in a naturally cooled structure such as cold frame or greenhouse, or in refrigerated storage. In either instance they are given a sufficient length of time for rooting above 50°F. (actually about 63°F.) before the temperature is dropped below 50°F. for six weeks (actually 35° to 45°F., depending on variety of lily).

It must be understood that the plant or plant part must be at a suitable stage of development when it is placed in a vernalizing temperature, or flowers may be imperfect or flowering may not occur. With azaleas and hydrangeas, well developed flower buds must be present before the plants are placed in the cool temperature. With some of the bulbs the bulb specialist may use various temperature regimes involving a period of time at high temperature so that the early stages of floral development occur before the cool temperature vernalization is given.

Cut flowers should be placed in warm water immediately after they are cut and then placed in temperatures below 50°F. for about 12 hours before being received by the consumer. The cut flower grower usually maintains his refrigerator at 45°F. for this short-term storage. Commonly this is referred to as hardening, and no doubt the name originated because the maximum amount of water has been absorbed by the cut flower and the tissues are firm or hard.

At some times cut flower or pot plant production is greater than market demand, and it is helpful to hold the produce in refrigerated storage until the market is more receptive. Cool temperatures slow growth and respiration, and thus the flowers and plants remain in good condition during the holding period. The holding temperature is 33° to 45°F., depending on the length of storage time. In some instances, cut flowers may be held for several days to a few weeks at 33°F., and for a long-term storage such as this the flowers are stored dry in airtight containers.

- ● THE AMOUNT OF WATER VAPOR IN THE AIR IS VARIABLE
  AND AFFECTS THE GROWTH OF PLANTS

The amount of water vapor in the air is expressed as per cent relative humidity, with 100 per cent relative humidity indicating that the air is saturated. At 50 per cent relative humidity, the air would have half as much water vapor as it would at saturation. The capacity of air for water vapor depends on temperature—the warmer the air temperature, the greater the amount of water vapor it can contain. For this reason it is important to list the temperature reading when a relative humidity determination is made. If 30°F. air at 100 per cent relative humidity was vented into a greenhouse and the temperature of that volume of air raised to 50°F., the relative humidity would be about 50 per cent, and if it were raised to 70°F. the relative humidity would be about 25 per cent.

Relative humidity determinations are usually made by observing the temperature difference between a dry-bulb and a wet-bulb thermometer and then using a chart which lists relative humidity values for the various temperature differences. The best dry-bulb-wet-bulb device for use in the greenhouse is the sling psychrometer. It has two similar thermometers mounted so they may be rotated by hand. One of the thermometers has a wick on the bulb which is moistened before rotation, and the rate of evaporation of water from the wick is dependent on the temperature and the amount of moisture in the air. When the air is saturated with water vapor there would be no temperature difference between dry and wet bulbs and 100 per cent relative humidity would be indicated. The greater the temperature difference between dry and wet bulbs, the lower the relative humidity. There are stationary units in which the wick of the wet bulb remains in a vessel containing water, but these are less reliable than sling psychrometers because of lack of air movement and eventual encrustation of salts in the wick. The result is less evaporation of water and less temperature difference between dry and wet bulbs. If it is necessary to use a stationary unit, the salt accumulation on the wick can be eliminated by using distilled water.

Control of the amount of water vapor in the greenhouse air is difficult, but considerably more control is possible than outdoors. Water vapor is added to the air when water changes from the liquid to the gas phase; and for this to occur, sources of water and heat are required. The frequent irrigations in the greenhouse and warm temperatures provide the means for maintaining high relative humidity. There are differences in facilities and methods of operation, however, resulting in varying amounts of moisture in the air in different greenhouses. To increase the relative humidity, water may be syringed frequently on plants and surroundings. It is possible to make further additions of moisture to the greenhouse air by use of mist; and the more finely the water is divided by the misting nozzle, the greater the quantity that is changed from the liquid to the vapor stage. To break up the water to that extent requires that it be ejected through a very tiny orifice under several hundred pounds' pressure per square inch. Most water available for use in the greenhouse has dissolved in it quantities of salts which precipitate out and cause plugging of the nozzles. Costs of equipment and maintenance of systems for adding mist directly to the greenhouse air are greater than can be justified commercially. This statement must not be construed to refer to all misting systems which may be used in the greenhouse. The reference is only to the systems designed to put mist into the air in such a way that it vaporizes immediately and increases relative humidity. The systems used for misting plants are designed for use primarily in propagation to maintain 100 per cent relative humidity in the immediate vicinity of the plants by keeping a constant covering of water on the plant surface. These systems are reasonable, and very effective for this specific use, and incidentally do increase the relative humidity of the total greenhouse atmosphere somewhat; but it is not possible to use them beyond the propagation stage because they keep plants and soil too wet.

It must be kept in mind that when water changes from the liquid to gas phase in the greenhouse, the temperature of air and/or surroundings is reduced accordingly. This is realized during hot weather because the fan and pad system used at that time was installed for the specific purpose of cooling the surroundings. The tendency at that time of the year is to overlook the fact that relative humidity is increased in accordance with the amount of cooling that takes place. During the cool season, although we may have only an increase in relative humidity in mind, we must be prepared to add heat to the greenhouse atmosphere to prevent chilling of air or plants as water evaporates or plants transpire.

Moisture is added to the air as plants transpire. Other conditions being equal, the relative humidity will be higher in a greenhouse containing large plants than in one that has small plants. The rate of water loss from the plant in transpiration depends on the water supply in the plant, the area of the stomate openings, the amount of water vapor in the air outside the leaf, and the temperature differential between leaf and air. In transpiration, plants lose heat and moisture because heat is removed from the plant as water evaporates from the plant through the stomates to the air. The loss of water from the plant regulates plant turgidity and the temperature of the plant, and in addition the transpiration stream distributes minerals absorbed by the roots from the highly fertile greenhouse soils in proportion to the rate of transpiration.

Frequently there is less moisture in the air outdoors than in the greenhouse, and the indoor air moisture is reduced by interchange of air. This occurs continuously to some degree because of structural design through the glass laps in greenhouses covered with glass, and in the course of temperature regulation through ventilators or exhaust fans. During cool weather, although the actual amount of water vapor per volume of air is not changed when outdoor air is introduced into the greenhouse, the relative humidity is reduced as the air is brought to greenhouse temperature. The relative humidity is further reduced as the warm air in the greenhouse contacts the inner surface of the glass and water vapor from the air condenses on the glass; and the greater the temperature differential between inside the greenhouse and outdoors, the greater the amount of water vapor that is removed from the air by this condensation. If the outdoor temperature is cool enough, ice and frost are formed on the inner surface of the glass. This does seal glass laps and reduce the amount of air interchange with the exterior, and it can be of considerable benefit if the weather is windy as well as cold. Frost on the glass, however, does reduce the amount of light transmitted into the greenhouse, and in northern climates when below-zero temperatures may exist continuously for several days there may be so much frost on the glass that it will be dark in the greenhouse in spite of the bright sunshine outdoors. The driest air experienced in the greenhouse will be at night during cold weather, and the high relative humidity usually will be at night in warm weather.

The reason for maintaining high relative humidity in the vicinity of greenhouse plants is to prevent undue water loss from plants by transpiration. Because a plant's stomates are closed during the dark, water loss from the plant during the night should be minimal, even if the relative humidity of the air is low; and thus attempts to maintain high humidity will be confined mainly to the daylight hours.

Some plant diseases are promoted in moist environments. Water vapor from the air will condense on plant surfaces if the plant is cooler than the air and provide the conditions suitable for the growth of some plant pathogens. When the source of heat disappears, the plant loses heat faster than the surrounding air, and if a new source of heat is not established promptly water may condense on the plant surface. To prevent this, greenhouse operators start the heating system before the sun disappears at evening. If some venting is done during this preliminary heating, the relative humidity of the air also will be reduced.

- **CARBON DIOXIDE IS ONE OF THE INGREDIENTS USED BY THE PLANT IN MAKING FOOD**

Carbon dioxide is available to the plant from two sources—from respiration within the plant and from the air surrounding the plant. If the plant is to increase in size, it is obvious that an external source of carbon dioxide is needed. The air normally contains .03 per cent (300 ppm) carbon dioxide, and diffusion through the stomates into the plant can occur when the stomates are open and the concentration of carbon dioxide in the plant is less than that of the air. Outdoors the concentration of carbon dioxide in the air remains uniformly at .03 per cent. In the greenhouse the amount of carbon dioxide per unit of air may vary, although with usual venting procedures the carbon dioxide concentration is approximately the same inside and outside the greenhouse. During cold weather, with no venting during the day, it is conceivable that the carbon dioxide concentration in the greenhouse may be less than outdoors.

For years, experimental work had shown that growth could be promoted in some plants when the carbon dioxide concentration of the atmosphere was increased, but it was not felt that there was a workable commercial application. In recent years, much work has been done in various parts of the country to further investigate the commercial possibilities of increasing the carbon dioxide in greenhouse air, and this has resulted in rather common acceptance of the procedure for many greenhouse crops. Many of the recommendations are for maintaining approximately .1 per cent (1,000 ppm) carbon dioxide in the greenhouse atmosphere—although in some instances twice that concentration is proposed. Because the need for carbon dioxide is in photosynthesis, which takes place only in light, the enriched carbon dioxide atmosphere is used only at that time. Stomates normally open in the light, and diffusion of greater quantities of carbon dioxide into the plant could be expected. It is possible to maintain higher levels of carbon dioxide in the greenhouse only when the structure may be tightly closed during the day, and thus its use in warm climates may be very momentary. In the colder North, supplementary carbon dioxide may be added to the greenhouse air from around November to May.

Once the general relationship of light and carbon dioxide in plants is recognized, it is easy to become overly enthusiastic about the possibilities of adding more and more carbon dioxide to the greenhouse atmosphere. It is relatively easy to add the carbon dioxide—but only at the time of the year when the available light is low, which limits the rate of photosynthesis and the need for carbon dioxide. There are definite limits to the usefulness of increasing the carbon dioxide concentration in the greenhouse environment. With some plants there are no apparent beneficial effects—several growers report no increase in quality or quantity with the Forever Yours rose but some response with other varieties. Some of the most favorable results are reported with geraniums and snapdragons. With those two crops there seems to be no question but that .12 per cent (1,200 ppm) carbon dioxide should be used. A higher-quality crop is produced in a shorter period of time. Generally favorable results are reported with chrysanthemums and carnations, although there is considerable difference in response among the mum varieties.

Carbon dioxide may be added to the greenhouse air in several different ways. The most popular method is by means of generators. In most instances these are units originally designed as heaters but now used for the carbon dioxide they produce rather than the heat. Although these units are now labeled and considered CO_2 generators, the effects on the greenhouse atmosphere of the heat and water vapor they also produce should be evaluated. These generators may be either gas or fuel oil burners, but those that use gas are usually more trouble-free. If combustion is complete, oxygen will be consumed and carbon dioxide and water vapor will be produced. Adequate air inlets must be provided so that the oxygen supply is sufficient for complete combustion. Products of incomplete combustion may be damaging to plants or workers, or both. The quality of fuel is important, as sulfur is a rather common contaminant in fuels; and the product of combustion is sulfur dioxide, which is very damaging to plants.

Carbon dioxide may be purchased in the gas, liquid, or solid (dry ice) form, and the pure gas dispensed into the greenhouse air. This method may be a little more costly but certainly is very reliable.

Carbon dioxide is one of the products of decay (oxidation) of organic matter. Rose growers commonly use organic mulches on their benches, and it is possible that the carbon dioxide levels in these houses are higher than in ones in which there is no mulching. This may be of benefit to some rose varieties but of questionable help to Forever Yours and possibly others. It is not practical to use mulch on other greenhouse crops, so that source of carbon dioxide seems to be of limited worth.

It is possible to forecast the carbon dioxide concentration in the greenhouse air by making the necessary calculation. With generators, and knowing the kind of fuel and the rate of consumption, the quantity of CO_2 produced may be computed. The manufacturer of the generator should be able to supply this information. To maintain 1,000 ppm carbon dioxide in a greenhouse of 10,000 cubic feet, an input of about 10 cubic feet per hour of carbon dioxide would be required. The actual level maintained should be monitored periodically with equipment such as Mine Safety Appliances Universal Tester. This is a pump-type unit which passes a measured volume of air through a detector tube, and the length of color change indicates the concentration of carbon dioxide in the sampled air. Detector tubes may also be used for indicating concentrations of carbon monoxide or sulfur dioxide.

- ## A CONTINUOUS SUPPLY OF OXYGEN IS
  ## ESSENTIAL FOR PLANT GROWTH

The normal oxygen supply of the air of around 20 per cent seems to be adequate for plant growth and development. In standard greenhouse operations there is sufficient interchange with outdoor air so that the concentration of oxygen within the greenhouse and outdoors remains about the same. In the exceptional instances when glasshouses are frosted and closed for long periods of time, plastic houses are not ventilated regularly, or burners are used in tightly closed greenhouses, it is possible to have oxygen deficiency.

Oxygen is a by-product of photosynthesis in the plant, and in this way the plant supplies some of its own needs for oxygen. Depending on the concentration of oxygen within the plant and in the surrounding air, oxygen may diffuse into or out of the plant primarily through the stomates.

- ## AIR MOVEMENT MAY BENEFIT PLANT GROWTH

Regardless of whether ventilators are open or closed, some air movement in the greenhouse should be beneficial to plant growth. Without adequate air movement the physical characteristics of the air would be variable from one area to another—usually the relative humidity would be higher in the immediate vicinity of the plants, and the concentration of carbon dioxide during the day might be less.

If there is a temperature differential in an air mass there will be air movement because heated air expands, becomes lighter, rises, and is replaced by cool air. This may be considered natural air movement— or it might be better to term it the natural result when heat is added to air. It is a means of transference of heat, and this type of air movement is referred to as convection currents. On a summer night with little air movement outdoors and no temperature differential between the greenhouse air and outdoors, there will be virtually no air movement within the greenhouse and practically no interchange of air with the exterior. When the temperature outdoors is cooler than it is in the greenhouse, the air heated by the sun or the heating system establishes the convection currents bringing the warm air to the roof, where heat is transferred to the glass (and more than likely with this loss of heat, water is deposited on the inner surface of the glass); the cooled air then flows along the surface of the glass to the base of the greenhouse. If ventilators are open, some of the heated air will continue to rise and exit through the ventilators to the exterior, and some cool air from the exterior will enter the greenhouse through glass laps, other ventilators, or other portions of the ventilator. The natural air circulation serves a good purpose in greenhouse management, but in many instances additional benefits to plant growth result from the more positive control of air movement that is possible with the use of fans.

Air movement by mechanical means (fans) may involve the circulation of air that is present in the greenhouse, movement of air out of the greenhouse, or movement of air into the greenhouse. With fan and pad systems used during warm weather, the fans are exhaust type, and as the air from the greenhouse is removed it is replaced by air from outdoors coming through the pads. During the day when cooling is desired, water is trickled through the pads, and the temperature of the incoming air is reduced according to the amount of water evaporated. With dry pads and fans in operation there would be interchange of air with the exterior but no temperature reduction, and this method of operation is suitable during the night in warm weather. In the day about 10 cubic feet of air is moved per minute per square foot of greenhouse area, and at night about half of that air movement would be suitable.

The fans designed to circulate the air solely within the greenhouse (Nivola Dutch Mill and Turbulator) are installed overhead, and they move the air outward and downward. They are not used during fan and pad season if that system is installed, but at other times of the year the air circulation fans should be in operation continuously. They provide much more uniform air conditions throughout the house, and the air movement caused by these fans is about 4 cubic feet per minute per square foot of greenhouse area.

Some fans have been designed to either circulate the air within the greenhouse or to introduce some air from outdoors as well as circulate it with the air in the greenhouse (Tube-Vent and Fan-Jet). These tube-fan systems are installed with the fan close to one end of the greenhouse and toward the ridge. A perforated poly tube is attached to the tube and extends the length of the greenhouse, and a shutter is installed in the wall in back of the fan. The direction of air movement is into the tube, and if the shutter is closed it is solely air within the greenhouse that is circulated. If the shutter is open, air from outdoors is introduced and circulated along with the greenhouse air. The tube-fans should be operated continuously and the shutter motorized to open or close as controlled by thermostat. The thermostat would also control exhaust fans so that some air would be removed from the greenhouse as air from outdoors is being introduced. These fans provide air movement at about the rate of 2 cubic feet per minute per square foot of greenhouse area.

The fan and poly tube system, which uses exhaust-type fans and a perforated poly tube with open end attached to a shuttered opening in the side wall, is the cold weather counterpart of the fan and pad system that is used in warm weather. Only about half of the fans are used at a time (about 5 cubic feet per minute per square foot of greenhouse area), and if the shutter is open the tube fills with outdoor air. This system is not designed to circulate air within the greenhouse. It is used only to introduce air into the greenhouse from outdoors—solely a temperature-control device—, but it can be used very effectively for that purpose during cool weather.

• CONTROL OF PESTS AND DISEASES IS A CONSTANT CHALLENGE

All routes of control need to be used—avoidance, management of environment, chemical, and natural adversaries. The pest or disease problem starts with the introduction of the pest or pathogen to the greenhouse environment. Some pests can walk in (mice, ants, caterpillars), several fly in (moths, aphids, white flies), both pests and plant pathogens may float in (thrips, spores, or bits of pathogens), and many get the free trip—they are carried in on plants or equipment. Although the suddenness of some outbreaks seems to indicate spontaneous generation, there just is not such a thing; the problem started with an individual of its own kind and propagated to the extent that it was recognized as a problem. Avoid the admittance of pest or pathogen into the greenhouse and the problem is controlled. For the walkers, some may be excluded by barrier and others by making their walk longer—eliminate their breeding places outside the greenhouse by removing trash and weeds.

The fliers are difficult to intercept, and the best approach may be to make their flight as long as possible. The tomato patch outside the greenhouse may produce some swell juice and paste for Mom, but it also makes a short commuter trip for the white flies to the mums or poinsettias indoors. Eliminating some of the attractants indoors may help. Moths go for lights, and during the moth season it probably will help to use the yellow lights that do not attract them.

It may be possible to bar some of the floaters from entrance to the greenhouse by using tobacco cloth impregnated with suitable chemical over the ventilators or to use some chemicals in the pad water to discourage entry through the pad. It should help to keep trash piles as far as possible from the greenhouse and not on the windward side.

Many pest and disease problems originate with plants or equipment which is brought into the greenhouse. This could probably be prevented if everything could be routed through a delousing or fumigation chamber, but this does not seem to be practical commercially. The best procedure is to inspect everything as carefully as possible when it is brought in, and anything that looks suspicious should be isolated until it can be given a clean bill of health.

These various methods of avoidance of problems are very important now, and it appears that even more reliance will need to be placed on them in the future. The use of agricultural chemicals has been curtailed or severely limited by legislation from various levels of government, from the federal down through the municipal. Because of the constantly changing scene, it is not possible in a publication of this type to now list materials for the control of pests and diseases or to make recommendations on their use. This information must come from sources which are brought up to date daily—possibly the extension specialists in entomology and plant pathology.

● CORRECT MANAGEMENT OF THE ENVIRONMENT IS A WORKABLE COMMERCIAL
  MEANS OF CONTROLLING THE INCIDENCE OF DISEASE

Regulation of the environment gives no measurable control of pests. Oh, it is true that pests breed faster in higher temperatures, but the greenhouse temperatures must be regulated for best plant growth and most pests thrive at those temperatures also. It is possible, however, to limit the incidence of disease by making necessary adjustment in environmental conditions.

The diseases considered here are the ones confined primarily to the aerial portions of the plant. These would be such as leaf spots, petal blights, and some stem rots. The objectives are to so regulate the environment that the disease does not start, or if it does get a start, to limit its spread. In spite of attempts to exclude the plant pathogens from the greenhouse, there usually are sufficient spores present, and if environmental conditions are right they will start in growth and produce disease symptoms. Most of the plant pathogens grow satisfactorily at the same temperatures that are suitable for the crop plants, but they cannot start in growth until the moisture conditions are just right. It is these moisture conditions that must be correctly regulated. Rust on carnations and most bacterial diseases will not develop unless there is water on the plant part. The most common reasons for water on plants are drips from the roof or improper irrigation procedures. Diseases such as Botrytis blight and powdery mildew get their starts when these pathogens find themselves in just a film of moisture on the plant part—probably the moisture is not even visible. If temperature, humidity, and air movement are juggled in such a way that the film of moisture is prevented from forming, the pathogens will not start in growth.

Moisture does not form on the plant when the plant temperature is warmer than the air temperature. During the day when the sun is out, the plant temperature usually is higher than the air temperature; however, in cool weather the reverse may be true in the evening if the heating is not properly handled. Therein lies the reason for the old and still true admonition to start heating the houses before sundown, while still venting. This serves two purposes—a heat source for the plants is maintained, and some moisture-laden air is ejected from the greenhouse. Continuous air movement in the greenhouse can be of help because this mixes the more moist air in the vicinity of the plants uniformly with the rest of the air mass. During warm weather when the heating system is not in operation, sources of air moisture (irrigation late in the day, operation of wet-pad cooling) should be limited as much as possible, and continuous air circulation by means of fans provided.

- **CHEMICAL CONTROLS WILL NEED TO BE USED IN SPITE OF MOST CAREFUL OPERATION**

Avoidance and environment management are preventive-type programs. The use of chemicals may be on either a preventive or a see-and-treat program. There are strong advocates for each method, but the success of the program probably is dependent on how the operator adapts it to his situation. If management is perceptive and observant, the see-and-treat program—particularly for pests—should be the best.

Regardless of which program is used, it definitely must be established what pest or disease is being treated. On a preventive program the choice of materials to be used would be based on the troubles that would be most likely to occur—not on preventing anything and everything that could possibly take place. On mums the best decision may be to have no chemical preventive program for aboveground diseases, and to put aphid control on a preventive basis. Foliar and flower diseases and pests such as two-spotted mites or worms would be treated if observed. Some will argue that if the plants must be sprayed for aphid control, a fungicide plus a pesticide for spider or worm control might just as well be added. There is some merit to this reasoning, but there are also some potential problems. The more materials that are applied, the greater the chances of unsightly residues on the plant; and worse yet, the possibilities of actual damage to plant tissues or growth are increased. Depending on the problem, the treatment objectives and techniques may be different. Aphids usually are located toward the stem tips, and two-spotted mites start their infestation on the undersides of mature leaves, toward the bottom of the plant. Aphids seem to be controlled more readily with a coarse, low-pressure spray, and the mites with a high-pressure, fine spray. There will be times when combined treatments will be the best approach, but this should be evaluated each time, rather than the shotgun being used in the hope that everything good will happen.

When disease symptoms or pests are observed, they first must be identified so that control materials may be selected that will actually give control. Most pests are rather easily identified, but many of the disease symptoms are confusing. There are several look-alikes, and there are some that can look like something that never happened before. The greenhouse manager should have help with identifying diseases, and possibly some pests. The various state extension specialists not only should be able to identify the problem but should be able to recommend the best control and the methods for use. Expert and up-to-date assistance in this area of greenhouse operation is a vital need of the manager.

There may have been a day when a stomach poison would control various pests, a contact spray would asphyxiate a number of others, and a general fungicide would handle most diseases; but that day is far in the past. There are some fine specific controls available, but they are truly that—specific. A given material controls only one sort of thing, and groping and grasping will not help the situation. It can be expected that there may be only one material that really gives good control of a certain pest at a given time, but a few weeks later its effectiveness may be much less and another material may then be better.

Agricultural chemicals may be available in various forms—wettable powders, soluble powders, dusts, granules, emulsions (miscibles), aqua or flowable forms, aerosols, and fumigants. Some of the chemicals may be obtained in several forms and others in only one form. The method of application of the material may vary, depending on the form of it. Because of the necessity of using specific materials for specific troubles, the greenhouse manager must have the equipment on hand for spraying, dusting, fumigating, or applying aerosol. The operator who has decided to use only aerosol application because it costs less in labor, leaves no residue, and is effective needs to be ready to jump immediately to spraying if the effectiveness diminishes and the material that now works is available only in a form that must be sprayed.

Various methods are used for dispersing the pesticide to the site where the pest or plant pathogen is located. In spraying and dusting, usually the finely divided material is forcefully directed onto the plants, and the plan is to give as uniform and complete coverage of plant, pest, or pathogen as possible. If wettable powders are used for spraying, the liquid must be agitated constantly in order to keep the material in suspension. If the material is available in either wettable powder or emulsion form, the wettable powder should be used in the greenhouse. It will add some noticeable residue to the plants, but there is less possibility of plant damage. If aqua or flowable forms are available, they may be used safely and with no residue problem. The use of emulsions is particularly treacherous in very warm weather or in dark, cool weather. If it is necessary to use an emulsion in the greenhouse, it should be considered that under good weather conditions up to a pint of the emulsion per 100 gallons of water may be safe but that anything over that amount is very questionable. Never use two or more emulsions together. The chemicals themselves may be compatible, but the double quota of oil applied to the plants would most certainly cause serious plant damage some of the time. Many of the chemicals in wettable powder form are compatible and could be used in the same spraying if necessary,

Lots of crops have been lost because pesticides or fungicides were not measured correctly. Too often somebody decides that a 4-inch potful is about the right amount to put in the spray tank, when in fact it may be twice the recommended quantity—or in some instances basic mathematics is faulty, resulting in the wrong amounts being used. Whoever is doing the measuring and mixing must be cautioned to use extreme care because he is then handling the material in its most concentrated form, and if it is toxic to humans the hazard would be greatest at that time.

With the other methods of using pesticides, instead of the materials being applied directly to the plants it is dispersed into the air, and eventually the air laden with pesticide engulfs the plant. To get good, uniform dispersion throughout the air, the material must be dispensed as fine particles, there must be an active propellant, there must be a minimum of air movement, and the minimum air temperature should be 75°F. For aerosol application the propellant is a liquid when under pressure and a gas in atmospheric pressure. The pesticide is dissolved or in suspension in the propellant liquid, and when the valve is opened the liquid in the container changes to gas as it is expelled and carries the pesticides in finely divided particles with it. Aerosols must not be discharged directly at plants because that procedure will harm plant tissues. The aerosol method of application is fast and efficient, but unfortunately only certain materials can be handled this way.

The other methods of dispersing pesticides into the air use heat as the propellant. Some materials may be vaporized from the heating lines in the greenhouse or from burners designed for this purpose. There is only a limited number of chemicals that may be dispensed in this fashion. This method is fast and economical. Some pesticides can be mixed with combustibles and ignited. These are called fumigators, and again there are relatively few materials that can be handled in this way. It is a fast method of treatment and the most dramatic, as clouds of smoke billow up, making it clear that something is happening. Various fogging devices have been used in which the pesticide dissolved or suspended in oil is propelled by heat. This method is fast, but only a few materials can be used this way, and the equipment is somewhat temperamental.

The chemicals which may be used in pest and disease control range all the way from those that are completely harmless to humans to those that are extremely toxic. The manager must make sure that the people involved understand fully what they are doing and that protective gear is available and used. There are three routes by which the chemicals may get into a person's body—inhalation (breathing through mouth or nose), ingestion (eating or drinking), and dermal contact (exposure to the skin). There seems to be more awareness of the necessity for protection from inhalation, and yet the other forms of contact may be just as hazardous. Too many greenhouse operators seem to understand that a gas mask and protective clothing are needed for an aerosol application but are content to play Russian roulette with fumigating or spraying. Those that feel too confined or have a fear of getting into a gas mask should be advised that a respirator with chemical cartridges will give the same degree of protection from inhalation and ingestion that a gas mask will.

Timing is so important. With a fungicide application, it should be understood that the infected plants may not be cured, but hope-fully the progress of the disease will be limited. The best trick is to get the fungicide on before the pathogen starts in growth in the plant, or if an individual plant becomes involved, to be timely enough with the application so that the pathogen is stopped in its tracks before it reaches the other plants. The name *fungicide* literally means fungus killer; however, some liberties have been taken in applying this term to materials used in treating plant diseases, and not all of the "fungi-cides" actually are lethal to fungi. Some delay or curtail the growth of the pathogens, and these are more properly called *fungistats*. It is im-portant to know the true characteristics of the material being used—applications of fungistats will need to be made more often than those of fungicides.

Pesticides will not necessarily control all stages of development of the pest. Some inactivate the eggs and not the adults—others the adults and not the eggs. Or young adults may be controlled rather easily, but more mature ones only with difficulty. Timing may be as important as the kind of material that is used. With many pests, more complete control results from a series of at least three applications, spaced three or five days apart. Single applications on a monthly basis may prevent engulfment by the pest but often will maintain too high a pest population.

A record should be kept which would include date, time of day, what was used, how much was used, who did it, temperature in the greenhouse, and general weather conditions. Such a record would make it possible to determine when to treat again, or why the pest or disease was not controlled, or if the application may have been the cause of plant damage.

● PROBLEMS IN PLANT GROWTH AND DEVELOPMENT
  REQUIRE DELIBERATE ANALYSIS

When there appears to be a problem with plant growth or de-velopment, the situation must be analyzed carefully enough so that a correct diagnosis can be made and the proper action taken. The appearance (symptoms) of the above-the-ground portions of the plant is the evidence of a problem, and if there is a problem there must be a cause for it. The cause of the plant problem may be discovered if the symptoms are properly evaluated. Knowing the cause of the problem, proper treatment may then be used to relieve the problem.

- **THE GREENHOUSE MANAGER MUST KNOW HOW TO EVALUATE SYMPTOMS OF PLANT PROBLEMS**

Symptoms frequently are not clear-cut. It may be a matter of degree or extent. It must be established first if the symptom is meaningful, and this usually can be done by comparing the plant in question with others of the same kind growing under similar conditions in the same vicinity.

Other than the observed deviation (symptom), do the plant's roots and top seem to have normal growth and development? If there are other symptoms, consideration should be given to their possible relationship.

Some symptoms may have various causes.

It is important to determine timing. When would the cause have had to be in effect to produce the symptom? Sometimes it is possible to "read the plant" in order to set timing (today's mature leaves were last month's tip leaves, or the position of leaf size and stem diameter in the plant indicates moisture and mineral quantities in the plant at that time of growth, etc.).

Usually some witch hunting for causes can be eliminated by estimating whether the problem came to the plant through the air or through the soil. In many instances it will be quite clear that for the type of trouble, the cause just had to have a specific route, and acknowledging the route narrows the search.

- **SOME CAUSES OF PLANT PROBLEMS ARE ROUTED THROUGH THE AIR**

The most common causes of problems that affect plants through the air are temperature, moisture, gases, plant pathogens, light, pests, and miscellaneous others.

Plant problems may be caused by temperatures that are too low or too high. Plants in too low temperatures may have large flower buds on short, heavy growth. Flower and leaf colors are more intense, but time of flowering may be delayed. Plants in too high temperatures typically have short, thin stems and small flowers. In some instances flowering will be accelerated and in others, delayed. Leaves will be small and thin, and leaf and flower colors faded.

With excessive moisture in the air, leaf, stem, and flower diseases are more prevalent and growth of plants is lush and soft. When there is too little moisture in the air, leaves and flowers may be small and growth hard.

Problems from gases in the air may originate right at the greenhouse with products of incomplete combustion from the boiler room or from unit heaters or carbon dioxide generators located in the greenhouses. These gases may cause flower malformation or failure to flower. Excesses of sulfur dioxide may develop from combustion sources within the greenhouse or from adjacent manufacturing plants. The primary symptom of excess sulfur dioxide is flower or leaf burn.

Some of the disease symptoms caused by plant pathogens descending on plants through the air are characteristic and well known, and others are difficult to confirm. In all instances it is necessary to obtain positive identification of the pathogen causing the problem so that specific steps can be taken to eliminate or control it. Most greenhouse managers should need and know where to seek help in identifying the causes of plant diseases.

Plant problems caused by light are usually concerned either with the quantity of light available to the plants or the daily length of light and dark periods. If the light quantity is too great the symptoms may be similar to those in plants in too high temperatures. In extreme conditions there may be some burn on flowers or leaves. When there is not enough light quantity, the plant usually has fewer stems, growth is slow, stems are of small diameter, and leaves are thin. When plants are in the wrong day length, flowering is prevented in qualitative plants and delayed in quantitative plants. Variable day length produces deformed flower buds in qualitative plants and delayed flowering in quantitative plants.

Most pests causing a problem can be seen and identified. However, some are difficult to observe, such as thrips within flowers, cyclamen mites which are too small to be seen, leaf nematodes within leaves, and pests that migrate daily, such as slugs or some larvae or worms. Positive identification of pests is necessary in order to select the proper pesticide for controlling them. In some instances the pest may be identified by the characteristic damage to the plant.

There are many miscellaneous causes of plant problems. Damage from the incorrect use of pesticides is a common one. The greenhouse manager must understand and appreciate the potential hazards as well as the benefits of using pesticides on plants.

When fertilizer is applied improperly so that particles of it remain on the leaves, flowers, or stems of plants, those areas of the plants will appear burned. In extreme cases stems and, possibly, the entire plant may die.

Most greenhouse crop plants can be damaged or killed by herbicides which are being used to control weeds in an adjacent area. With many herbicides the fumes may pass through the air and damage plants at some distance from the point where the weeds are being treated. Equipment used for applying herbicides must never be used subsequently for applying pesticides or fertilizer to greenhouse crop plants.

Drips from steam or hot water pipes, oil or grease from ventilator machines, or glass cleaning materials have all been known to cause damage to greenhouse plants.

• SOME CAUSES OF PLANT PROBLEMS ARE ROUTED THROUGH THE SOIL

Causes of plant problems involve soil air, moisture, minerals, plant pathogens, plant pests, temperature, and miscellaneous others.

The most common aboveground plant symptoms of troubles originating in the soil indicate moisture and mineral deficiency in the plant. These symptoms include small flowers and leaves, short stems, fewer stems, dull colors, and hard growth. The moisture and mineral deficiency symptoms might in fact be caused by lack of moisture or minerals in the soil—or they may be caused by failure of the moisture and minerals in the soil to enter the plant because of lack of roots on the plant. The causes of poor root systems may be lack of air in the soil, water-saturated soil, an over-supply of minerals, plant pathogens, or plant pests. The manager must be able to judge the air and moisture characteristics by inspecting the soil. The mineral content of the soil should be verified by testing. If the roots have been damaged by plant pathogens or plant pests, the positive identification of pathogen or pest may have to be made by a specialist before proper treatment can be made.

If soil temperatures are too low during propagation or after planting, root development will be slow and top development will also be delayed.

The commonplace use of herbicides in field soils can present a problem for greenhouse plants if these soils are brought into the greenhouse. The weedkiller that the farmer uses successfully with corn or soybeans may be damaging or lethal to greenhouse crop plants.

- **TO BE EFFECTIVE THE TREATMENTS USUALLY HAVE TO BE SPECIFIC**

The specific cause of the trouble must be known, and the best specific treatment for the control of the problem used. General treatments, however well-intentioned, may aggravate rather than relieve the problem.

Sometimes more than one type of control may be used. In some instances the cause can be excluded, and this should be done if possible. The next level of control should be regulation of the environment—light, temperature, moisture, air, and minerals. Very often if this approach to the problem is used, chemical treatments will not be needed.

Timing of treatments may be worth as much as or more than the corrective action itself.

Reference Reviews

1. Anonymous, *Commercial Production of Pot Plants*, Bulletin 112, Her Majesty's Stationery Office, London, 1969. *The sections on ventilation, shading, and artificial illumination will be of interest. There are specific references to several pot plant crops.*
2. Anonymous, *A Manual of Carnation Production*, Bulletin 151, Her Majesty's Stationery Office, London, 1967. *Sections of Part II discuss management procedures, such as temperature, cold storage, carbon dioxide, and lighting.*
3. Canham, A. E., *Artificial Light in Horticulture*, Centrex Publishing Company, Eindhoven, The Netherlands, 1966. *Specific recommendations are given for the use of supplementary light for various crops as well as the growing of plants without daylight.*

4. Ecke, Paul, Jr., and O. A. Matkin, *The Poinsettia Manual,* Paul Ecke Poinsettias, Encinitas, California, 1971. *Much of the air management recommendations for poinsettias in this manual has application to other greenhouse crops.*

5. Gray, Harold E., *Greenhouse Heating and Construction,* Florists' Publishing Co., Chicago, 1956. *Chapter 1, "Heating Principles," has a good presentation on the effects of heating on air circulation and relative humidity. Chapter 6, "Control Systems," gives methods for control of heating in the greenhouse.*

6. Holley, W. D., and Ralph Baker, *Carnation Production,* William C. Brown Company, Inc., Dubuque, Iowa, 1963. *Chapters 8 through 10 cover control of temperature, light, and carbon dioxide on this crop. Chapters 12 and 13 give thorough handling of carnation diseases and pests, and means of control.*

7. Langhans, Robert W., et al., *Carnations—A Manual of the Culture, Insects and Diseases, and Economics of Carnations,* New York State Extension Service, Ithaca, 1961. *Temperature relationships with carnations are given in chapters 8 through 10. Diseases and insects and the control for this crop are covered in chapters 13 and 14.*

8. _____, *Chrysanthemums—A Manual of the Culture, Diseases, Insects, and Economics of Chrysanthemums,* New York State Extension Service and New York State Flower Growers Association, Inc., Ithaca, 1964. *Management of light and temperature for chrysanthemums is critical, and the subject is well covered in chapters 11 and 12. Chapter 15, "Diseases," and Chapter 16, "Insects," give thorough treatment and are well illustrated.*

9. _____, *Snapdragons—A Manual of the Culture, Insects and Diseases, and Economics of Snapdragons,* New York State Extension Service and New York State Flower Growers Association, Inc., Ithaca, 1962. *Some of the specific applications of light and temperature to snapdragons are given in Chapter 9. The diseases and insects that commonly are a problem with snapdragons are presented in chapters 12 and 13.*

10. Langhans, Robert W., and D. C. Kiplinger, et al., *Easter Lilies—The Culture, Diseases, Insects, and Economics of Easter Lilies,* New York State Extension Service, Ithaca, and Cooperative Extension Service, Ohio State University, Columbus, 1967. *Management of temperature is discussed in several chapters—Chapter 4, "Factors Affecting Flowering," Chapter 5, "Present Methods of Handling Bulbs," Chapter 6, "Natural Cooling Method of Handling Bulbs," and Chapter 10, "Timing." Light management is given in Chapter 9, and diseases and insects in chapters 11 through 13.*

11. Laurie, Alex, D. C. Kiplinger, and Kennard S. Nelson, *Commercial Flower Forcing,* Seventh Edition, McGraw-Hill Book Company, New

York, 1969. *Chapter 4, "Factors Influencing Plant Growth," is a clear and concise discussion of botany and plant physiology, with special reference to greenhouse commercial flowering plants, and Chapter 5, "The Control of Enviromental Factors Influencing Plant Growth," has general recommendations for controlling the greenhouse environment. Management of the air environment for specific crops is given in chapters 9 through 13.*

12. Mastalerz, John W., et al., *Geraniums—A Manual on the Culture, Diseases, Insects, Economics, Taxonomy, and Breeding of Geraniums*, Second Edition, Pennsylvania Flower Growers, University Park, 1971. *Some general comments on management of the air environment are given in Chapter 9, and specific references and recommendations are made in chapters 11 through 17. Foliage diseases are covered in Chapter 18.*

13. Mastalerz, John W., Robert W. Langhans, et al., *Roses—A Manual of the Culture, Management, Diseases, Insects, Economics and Breeding of Greenhouse Roses*, Pennsylvania Flower Growers, University Park, New York State Flower Growers Association, Inc., Ithaca, and Roses, Inc., Haslett, Michigan, 1969. *Chapters 15 and 16 give good coverage of the effects of environmental conditions on roses and how they may be controlled. Chapter 17, "Physiological Disorders," is of interest because it describes and illustrates some of the harmful effects from the environment. The relationship between the air environment and the incidence of disease is clearly presented in chapters 22 through 24.*

14. Miller, Robert O., D. C. Kiplinger, et al., *Poinsettias—Culture and Use as Potted Plants*, Extension Bulletin S. B. 15, Ohio State University, Columbus, 1963. *Regulation of the air environment for this crop is given for stock plants, propagation, and flowering plants.*

15. Nelson, Kennard S., *Flower and Plant Production in the Greenhouse*, The Interstate Printers & Publishers, Inc., Danville, Illinois, 1967. *An introduction to botany and plant physiology is given in Chapter 3, "How the Surroundings Affect Plant Growth," and specific reference to the relationship between environment and crop plants are given in chapters 5 through 8.*

16. Salisbury, Frank B., and Cleon Ross, *Plant Physiology*, Wadsworth Publishing Company, Inc., Belmont, California, 1969. *The commercial grower may not be interested in each page of this well written but detailed text, but there are many sections of it that are invaluable. The following chapters are suggested for a start: Chapter 3, "Energy Relations and Diffusion," Chapter 13, "Photosynthesis," Chapter 14, "Carbon Dioxide Fixation and Photosynthesis in Nature," Chapter 15, "Respiration," Chapter 19, "Growth and the Problems of Morphogenesis," Chapter 20, "Mechanisms and Problems of Developmental Control," Chapter 21, "Plant Hormones and Growth Regulators," Chapter 23,*

"Photomorphogenesis," Chapter 24, *"The Biological Clock,"* Chapter 25, *"Responses to Low Temperature and Related Phenomena,"* Chapter 26, *"Photoperiodism and the Physiology of Flowering,"* and Chapter 27, *"Reproduction, Maturation, and Senescence."*

CHAPTER 7

Management of Marketing

CHAPTER 7

If production is to be successful, marketing must precede it—not all of the marketing process, just the portion of marketing that determines what and where the market is and plans the product accordingly. The purpose of the manufacturer (yes, flower and plant producers may be considered manufacturers) is to sell products—not to make products which might sell. Regardless of how good the product is, until it is sold and customers' needs have been satisfied, the manufacturer's objectives will not have been realized.

- **THE FLOWER AND PLANT GROWER NEEDS TO EVALUATE THE MARKET POTENTIAL BEFORE HE SETS UP SHOP**

The retail grower would have to use different methods in evaluating the market than the wholesale grower would, but in either instance they must use a realistic approach rather than one that is either overly optimistic or overly pessimistic. The retailer probably would want to visualize his sales area on the basis of the customers who would come to the greenhouse as well as those who would do business by telephone. The proposed location would have considerably more effect on the drive-in business than on the call-in. If there are retail florists in this sales area, is there good evidence that they are not fulfilling the needs of the customers? Because of product, location, service, price, or other factors, is it probable that a better job could be done of satisfying the needs of these customers? The financial success of the existing retailers may provide some clues on the potential of the market. Comparing their degree of success with the manner in which they operate their business should give some evaluation of the possibilities for additional sales in that area. If it appears that the primary business will be call-in, inquiries should be made about the possibilities of local means of promotion and whether national ordering service franchises may be available for the area.

After the type of market and the general needs of the customers have been established, this information can be used in planning production in the greenhouse. It is not possible for the retail grower to supply all of his flower and plant needs from his own greenhouse, but he should plan the production so that everything grown in the greenhouse is sold through his own retail shop. The retail grower needs to grow at his own greenhouse the flowers and plants that he could raise better or more cheaply than those he could obtain on the wholesale market.

Market determination for the wholesale grower is quite different. He does not necessarily need to be in the same geographical location as his market. Improvements in transportation have encouraged wholesale growers to locate in areas with favorable climate or labor conditions in spite of being some distance from the market. This in no way implies that distance from the market is no factor. In fact the reliability and cost of transportation from greenhouse to market must be evaluated along with the market potential.

The wholesale grower may sell his products to retailers or to wholesalers, or he may consign his flowers or plants to wholesalers who either deduct a commission from the selling price and remit the balance to the grower or submit a dump report on the items which did not sell and were discarded. Most wholesale grower sales to retailers are done on a local basis, although there are several examples of this type of marketing being handled from long distance. Long-distance shipping of cut flowers is more common than that of pot plants, although it is not unusual for pot plants to be transported a few thousand miles by truck to more favorable markets. It should be easier for the wholesale grower to establish what the market potential is because he deals with businessmen who should have experience and records on which to base their opinions. It would be appropriate to get a financial statement from these prospective customers. A favorable financial report would lend substance to their opinions on the market, and it would establish their ability to pay if flowers were sold or consigned to them.

Although this discussion has been in terms of establishing a flower and plant production business, market evaluation needs to be a continuing process. Either market area or product or both may have to be changed because of situations that arise. It usually is difficult for retail growers to move from the area in which they are doing business, but they may be able to change their methods of doing business or the products they handle sufficiently to continue a successful business.

Wholesale growers frequently have to change market areas in order to sell their product successfully, and through the years change in product also may be neccessary. This does not suggest change for change's sake, but change for the benefit of the business. It is easy to understand the reasons why changes were necessary in the past, but it is difficult to recognize or possibly accept the changes needed now or to forecast the ones of the future. Some product changes have been dictated by custom or style, such as the decline in demand for gardenias, orchids, and camellias with the reduced popularity of corsage wearing, or the increase in demand for bedding plants and hanging baskets caused by the movement to suburban living. Why did corsages fall in favor? Changing fashions may have had something to do with it—or maybe there is not enough to pin them to any more. Or is it possible the merchant priced them out of the field or made them so large that they would no longer really fill the need? It might be a combination of some of these things, or it could be that corsages have been replaced with substitute products. There is good evidence that corsages for Mom have been replaced-sometimes with other flowers— a vase of cut flowers or a pot plant—, but in other instances it might have been items of clothing, jewelry, or candy. The corsages for the high school or college girls may have been replaced with a dinner or a late show. Was the interest in bedding plants really triggered by increased suburban living, or was it a planned program of breeding better plants, producing them in marketable units, and promotion? The chances are good that it was a combination of these events.

The market demand for roses declined a few years ago, and rose growers reacted by limiting their rose production areas. Subsequently the market for roses improved and rose producing areas were correspondingly increased. The cause for this is not entirely clear, but the decline did come at the time when the production of year-round chrysanthemum cut flowers was on the increase, and possibly this was one of the causes. Roses have had a history of a notoriously short vase life for the customer, and chrysanthemums are one of the best keepers. The revival of rose production was timed with the introduction of a new variety with many improved characteristics, including much better vase life. The rose market is 90 per cent or so hybrid tea roses— and mostly red color. There has been some increase in demand for sweetheart roses, but the bulk of interest still is in the larger cousin. Could promotion change this demand? The sweetheart roses have better vase life than the hybrid teas, and there are many beautiful colors available in both types of roses. Is it possible that roses other than the large, red rose could do a better job of satisfying the customer's needs?

Innovations in production procedures have an effect on the market place. One of the most notable of these was in the development of the procedures for producing chrysanthemum flowers at any time of the year. The chrysanthemum has considerable utility—there are many shapes, sizes, and colors, and as mentioned previously the flower has good keeping quality. Unfortunately the leaves have less longevity; and if the producer and sellers do not handle the cut flowers properly or promptly, the consumer has a long-lasting flower on stem devoid of leaves. This eventually will affect marketing of this product.

Introduction of improved products by selection or breeding has a stimulating effect on the flower and plant market. This was referred to earlier with bedding plants and roses. Some other examples are chrysanthemums, snapdragons, and poinsettias.

- **FLOWER AND PLANT MARKETING SHOULD BE ANALYZED ON THE BASIS OF THE FOUR "P'S"—PRODUCT, PROMOTION, PLACE, AND PRICE**

Successful marketing requires more than a product that is needed by a customer. He has to be aware that there is such a product which will satisfy his needs and wants, the product has to be where it is convenient for him to get it, and it has to be priced within the customer's concept of value for that need. Some of these needs and wants are physiological, such as the relief from hunger and pain, and other needs may be psychological, sociological, or cultural. The need or want for flowers or plants could involve any of the latter three. It is an emotional motive usually for satisfaction of the sense of sight or smell—or it might be sociability, or pride, or fear (well, at least the errant husband is supposed to be exhibiting fear when he purchases flowers for his wife). Regardless of terminology it is important that the flower producer and seller recognize that the customer has a need or want (maybe even a problem), and he may get satisfaction from the purchase of flowers or plants. This might be the best way this need could be satisfied, or it might be only one of the ways that it can be fulfilled. Yes, a customer may have a need to express sympathy, to show love, or to beautify a room and he may elect to do this with flowers or plants, or he may give a memorial, bestow a box of candy, or purchase a painting. He will satisfy his need with flowers or plants only as long as this method is better than an alternate means. In many situations flowers and plants are homogenous products—there are other products that compete with them in the market place.

- **THE PRODUCT MUST BE DESIGNED TO GIVE SATISFACTION TO THE CUSTOMER AND PROFIT TO THE PRODUCER**

Who is the customer? With the retail grower, this is not a question, because he sells directly to the ultimate customer. He should be tuned to the needs of the customer and best know how to satisfy these needs, but it is entirely possible that he is so involved in the business of selling products that he has lost sight of the customer's needs. Was sympathy really expressed by the large but poorly arranged, half-dead flowers for the funeral; and would love have been better portrayed to Aunt Ella by a dish garden rather than the short-lived daffodils and iris for her prolonged stay in the hospital?

With the wholesale grower who sells to a wholesaler or consigns through a wholesaler, there tends to be confusion as to whom the product should be designed for. Producer, wholesaler, and retailer all have to be interested in whether the product is satisfying the needs of the ultimate consumer, but along the line the picture becomes distorted by special needs or wants for the wholesaler, and these are followed by others from the retailer. The wholesaler may want the roses cut so tight that they will not open even if he does not sell them immediately, and prefers to ignore the fact that they may never open for the consumer either. Or the retailer may demand 36-inch stems on chrysanthemums, although he never uses them longer than 20 inches in arrangements.

The product has to be designed for the ultimate consumer, and communication among producer, wholesaler, and retailer has to be good enough so that the objective is known and understood. The producer must understand that the ultimate customer will not know how well his product will fill the needs unless someone tells the customer about it. Who is going to tell the customer? The retailer is in the position to do it but does not necessarily have the information or the desire to do it. The producer's responsibility has to extend through the successful use of the product by the ultimate consumer, and this includes backing the product with enough promotion so that wholesaler, retailer, and customer know not only the product, but how it will fill needs.

Do customers have needs that can be satisfied with flowers and plants? Yes. Good evidence of this resulted a few years ago when flowers were included in an evaluation by a panel of homeowners in Columbus who had been used for testing desirability of several different kinds of food. Whether the food was beans, a top-quality ice cream, or a premium brand of chocolates, some panel members expressed no need or want for the product. When flowers were offered to the same panel, the expressed need was unanimous.

Flowers and plants have various qualities, and the degree to which these qualities satisfy customers needs varies with the individual and with the current need. Customers may have interest in and gain satisfaction from flower and plant qualities such as color, shape, odor, size, trueness to type, life and maturing, or association. These are all qualities of individual flowers or plants. Arrangements of flowers may have additional qualities. Flower producers tend to evaluate the effect of flowers purely on the basis of the flowers. Retail shop operators or flower designers are inclined to consider their arrangement of flowers and other items as having artistic qualities, with the individual flower qualities being of importance only as they contribute to the over-all design. Some customers get more satisfaction from the art work, and others purely from flowers or plants. The good flower and plant merchant will be able to sense the need and be able to satisfy it with the right product.

Flower color is an important quality because of the effect it has on customers. Certain colors may be more attractive to the eye, or in many instances there is a personal association of some kind with color. The color may be associated in the customer's mind with religious observance, such as white or yellow for Easter and red for Christmas; with an emotion such as love—quite often red, but not always—; or with the season of the year, such as bronze for fall. In recent years there has been some kind of marathon to tint, dye, or paint flowers all colors of the rainbow. The effect is not always good on the customer, but apparently it does satisfy some. Leaf color is also an important quality. Dark green leaves seem to have universal appeal, but there is considerable interest in variegated leaves also. It is difficult to explain why more customers seem to prefer red hydrid tea roses, white or yellow standard mums, white or pink snapdragons, and yellow pot mums. It is hard to believe that it is color itself that conditions this response. Possibly this color preference was created because only those colors were available when the flower was introduced on the market—or maybe it could be that flowers of that color have or had other qualities which are better.

Customers choose flowers and plants by shapes. Some like uniform and symmetrical shapes, and other like irregular or unusual shapes. With flowering pot plants the customer may respond to the shape of the entire plant structure as well as to the shape of the individual flowers.

In general scented flowers have more appeal than those with slight odor. There are definite customer preferences, however, for scents. Some individuals will enjoy the fragrance of the rose or snapdragon, but find the gardenia's odor a bit heady. There may be some associations based on scent—the Easter lily scent is understandably identified with Easter, and the carnation may remind some of funerals simply because for many years carnations were used commonly in set pieces.

Among producers, wholesalers, and retailers there is a direct relationship between size and quality—the larger the flower and the longer the stem, the better the quality of the flower. It is questionable if the consumer recognizes this same relationship. Size of flower or plant does bring him varying degrees of satisfaction, but he does not necessarily find that the larger items suit his purposes the best. It is possible that the size-quality concept originated with the size difference between poorly grown and well grown crops, with the carry-over judgement that short stems or small flowers indicate something less than good. To add to it, probably the easiest quality to rate is size—so if the flowers or plants are graded, size is one of the criteria used, and it may be the only one. This size-quality (and price) relationship with standard chrysanthemums will serve as an example. Traditionally they are graded by diameter of flower—4-inch, 5-inch, or 6-inch—with about a 36-inch stem length. The flower designer and the consumer have only limited use for a stem that long; but in spite of this, the size-quality concept is so firmly ingrained in the minds of flower wholesalers and retailers that regardless of flower size those with shorter stems will be considered of inferior quality. Standard varieties which do not normally produce flowers of 4 inches or more in diameter become classed as an inferior grade regardless of how desirable the flower color or shape may be. Large size does not necessarily indicate high quality in standard mums any more than intermediate or small size relates to lower quality. It is entirely possible that the producer will need to charge more for long-stemmed flowers or large-size plants because more growing time has been involved, but there is no good reason why smaller size should place any stigma on the other qualities of flowers and plants.

Trueness to type may mean something quite different to the customer than it does to the producer. The customer may have a concept of flower size, color, shape, or other qualities, and if the product is not true to this type, he may not be completely satisfied. The customer, and possibly the wholesaler and retailer too, may have some misconceptions about trueness to type. When this occurs it will take some good communication and promotion to change the concept. When chrysanthemums were first flowered out of season, it took some conversation before sellers and consumers would accept this as typical. Roses-are-red-and-violets-are-blue types of connotations may have some good features, but it also limits the market if sellers and customers do not realize some of the other possibilities.

The life and maturing qualities of flowers and plants bring satisfaction to the customers. Some people like flowers better at one stage of development, but most others enjoy watching the flowers develop and mature. Growth and maturing of plants are of interest to customers. Manufacturers sometimes refer to planned obsolescence of their product. There frequently is a direct relationship between price and the lasting quality of the product. Possibly they could make a unit that would last 10 times as long, but the purchase price would not be popular, or maybe the customer wants a shorter service life, or possibly the product would become obsolete because of change of style or design. There is built-in obsolescence in flowers and plants. This is generally understood and appreciated by customers. They do not expect nor want this product to last forever, but they do want to be able to enjoy it for a period of time that is somewhat normal for the particular flower or plant. Regardless of the other fine qualities that the flower or plant might have, the customer's need will not be satisfied if the flower or plant product becomes obsolete before its day. Flowers and plants have varying rates of perishability, but producer, wholesaler, and retailer must make every effort to assure that the product is in the hands of the consumer in good condition so that he may get full satisfaction from the life and maturation of it.

Flowers and plants usually are not packaged in the manner of manufactured goods. Any wrapping or packaging is used only as a temporary means of protection for the plant material. If a similar degree of protection can be afforded by transparent material, it is used, because that displays the product advantageously. The package does need to contain a marketable number of the product, it must provide protection during transportation and sales, and it is good if it allows display of the flower or enhances the display.

The use of brand name or trade-mark is not common with flowers and plants, but in the few instances where it has been used the effect has been beneficial. It seems that several segments of the industry might benefit their business by developing brand names for their products.

• WITHOUT PRODUCT PROMOTION THE CONSUMER MAY NEVER KNOW HOW WELL FLOWERS AND PLANTS CAN SATISFY HIS NEEDS

There are instances in which the consumer searches for and finds the product that he needs or that will be helpful to him; but it usually is more efficient and satisfactory for both consumer and producer if the word about the product is well enough circulated so that the customer knows how the product will help him and what he must do to obtain it. The amount of product promotion that is used with business in general varies all the way from none at all to too much. The flower and plant industry as a whole does not use enough promotion. Unfortunately, to the minds of some, *promotion* means using devious and questionable methods to trick or force the consumer into accepting the product. Perhaps another term should be used, such as *product apprisal,* which would imply the bringing of information about the product.

Regardless of terminology, communication does need to be good enough from producer, through wholesaler, through retailer, to consumer so that the various qualities of the product are well known and so that all concerned will understand how the product will satisfy customer needs. The message has to get all the way to the customer, and it should get there most effectively through regular sales channels. The sellers, however, will need to get the word first from the producer, and they probably will transmit the message better if they are given a workable routine for doing it. Word of mouth product apprisal serves some purpose, but the effect is not nearly so thorough and is much more temporary than the written word. Demonstration with the actual product is even better. For example, a well designed leaflet on a new rose variety may be a good aid in promoting sales for this new product; but in addition, if the producer gives some wholesalers and retailers a few of the roses to observe in their own homes, they will be more enthusiastic promoters. Or possibly the new rose could be displayed where potential customers could see it and read about it.

Flower and plant promotion must do more than tell what the product is. The potential customer is not necessarily interested in the flower or plant as such, but he could be very receptive to suggestions on how he can express love to his wife, or thanks to Aunt Thelma, or sympathy to a bereaved neighbor. What is the product that will give him this help? Where can he get it, and probably how much will it cost? Product promotion, which consists of an ad in the paper to "patronize your allied florist" or the bumper sticker that intones "eat more beef," is worthless because it gives a rather impertinent order to the customer without really offering any help for his needs.

- **THE PRODUCT MUST BE IN A PLACE THAT IS READILY AVAILABLE TO THE CUSTOMER**

We may drive 20 miles for a fine dinner in good surroundings but not be willing to go more than 6 blocks for a hamburger at a lunch counter. What place or places are best suited to handle the needs of flower and plant customers? It probably depends on the needs of the customer or whether the flowers require designing and delivery. Many of the special-occasion flowers and plants are ordered by telephone, and the customer may not necessarily feel the need for a close location. However, for incidental flowers and plants, he may want to drop in and browse; and this would require a place that the customer would class as being easy to get to, with adequate parking space, and a good sales area.

For the everyday use of flowers and plants in the home, the product requirements are quite different from those for special occasions; and the place where they will be sold most successfully is also different. These are products that the customer shops for and expects to carry home. It seems most likely that this sales place for flowers and plants should be as accessible as the grocery market; however, at this place the flowers will have to be handled so that they will be displayed adequately and kept in good condition.

- **MANY CUSTOMERS RELATE PRICE AND SATISFACTION**

The customer will not necessarily satisfy his needs at any price. Usually the first desire is to take care of the need, but there may be a period of evaluation in which the customer compares alternate products, their price, and the relative values. Within certain price limitations the demand for flowers and plants is inelastic—on the wholesale market just as many pot mums would be sold at $2.25 as at $2.00; or to look at it the other way, no more pot mums would be sold if the price were dropped from $2.25 to $2.00. There may be some room for argument here; and if there is, each pricer should determine just how elastic the demand is for flowers and plants. Would the demand at the lower price develop just as many or more total dollars? If not, it would not seem wise to use the lower price.

How are wholesale prices established? If the producer has handled the business procedures as he should, he will know product costs; and this will give him a basis for setting price. Theoretically he would add sufficient mark-up to the product cost so that selling costs would be met and there would be a profit remaining. In some instances it may be wise to make adjustments in price in accordance with a competitor's pricing or with market demand, but this should be done only if the results are beneficial. Probably the competitor's product is not comparable and should be priced differently. The effect market demand should have on price of flowers and plants is difficult to evaluate. If demand is not elastic and does not fluctuate with price, dropping price will not increase demand. In fact, in periods of low demand a price rise may be indicated, because if the demand is truly inelastic, just as many flowers would be purchased and the total number of dollars would be greater. This seems to run contrary to general concepts of supply-and-demand pricing, but it is entirely possible that flowers and plants do not fit the general situation.

It might be closer to the truth to view the wholesale market as a collection of customer types, each type having inelastic demands within certain price ranges. The total effect then would be toward elasticity of demand for flowers and plants, and the price would tend to fluctuate with supply. For a given price range or product, the wholesale merchant would know the potential demand for each group of customers. When that demand is met and the supply is not exhausted, the price is adjusted, creating a potential demand with another series of customers. Among these latter customers wlll be some who have developed elastic retail demand—more product can be sold when the price is lower.

There is some possibility that the producer might help generate demand at the retail level and thus make buying at the wholesale level more elastic. If this is to be done, it requires something more than lowering price. The producer must develop an entire promotion (appraisal?) package that the retailer can put into effect to increase retail sales. The retailer with a history of inelastic demand will not be swept over into elastic demand simply because of lower wholesale prices or greater supply of flowers. It is not necessarily that he is stubborn or ignorant; but his present retail customers have had set needs for flowers, and they will have to be made aware of how other needs can be satisfied, or it may be possible that a different group of customers could be reached.

Most flower and plant producers have need for alternate means of selling their products—at a profit. For instance, the wholesale producer who sells directly to retailers may have some retailers of a different type to whom he sells infrequently when supply exceeds demand. Usually this would be at a reduced price but on the basis of a greater quantity per sale. Whereas standard sales and pricing would be by the bunch or per 100, the special marketing would be by the 1,000 or truck load. The wholesale grower who consigns his products to wholesale commission houses usually will have alternate houses in other areas to which he can ship when the local market is oversupplied. This can be effective, unless the oversupply is general. Retail flower and plant producers should scale their production to their own flower shop needs, but there will be times when there is an excess produced which cannot be handled through the shop. Some retail growers consign the excess through local commission houses, but this is generally an unsatisfactory procedure. A better means of selling this excess production probably would be to other retail businessmen for decorations or for promotional work in their business; or possibly some service club promotions could be developed.

• DOES VERTICAL INTEGRATION BENEFIT MARKETING?

There has been increased interest in vertical integration, in which the producer maintains control of the product until it is successfully in the hands of the consumer. There are some convincing arguments for vertical integration. It should provide for better understanding, less waste motion, better communication, and more effective selling. It is a method of operation that probably should be considered by wholesale producers (retail producers are already somewhat vertically integrated), but it should not be considered a panacea for all. A good producer does not necessarily make an effective seller.

If the flower and plant producer does not maintain control of the product through sale to the ultimate consumer, he certainly must keep detailed interest in the product and how it is being handled by wholesalers and retailers. He must also know how well the product did satisfy the customers' needs.

Reference Reviews

1. Anonymous, *Commercial Production of Pot Plants*, Bulletin 112, Her Majesty's Stationery Office, London, 1969. *The comments on marketing in the manual are quite brief.*
2. Anonymous, *A Manual of Carnation Production*, Bulletin 151, Her Majesty's Stationery Office, London, 1967. *The sections on flower grading, packing, and marketing as practiced in Great Britain will be of interest to readers in this country.*
3. Holley, W. D., and Ralph Baker, *Carnation Production*, William C. Brown Company, Inc., Dubuque, Iowa, 1963. *Chapter 11, "The Handling and Marketing of Cut Flowers," is of particular interest because of the detailed information on all phases following harvesting of the flowers.*
4. Langhans, Robert W., et al., *Carnations—A Manual of the Culture, Insects and Diseases, and Economics of Carnations*, New York State Extension Service and New York State Flower Growers Association, Inc., Ithaca, 1961. *Chapter 16, "Grading and Marketing," discusses only the grading of carnations.*
5. —————————————————, *Chrysanthemums—A Manual of the Culture, Diseases, Insects, and Economics of Chrysanthemums*, New York State Extension Service and New York State Flower Growers Association, Inc., Ithaca, 1964. *Grading methods for chrysanthemums are given in Chapter 18.*
6. —————————————————, *Snapdragons—A Manual of the Culture, Insects and Diseases, and Economics of Snapdragons*, New York State Extension Service and New York State Flower Growers Association, Inc., Ithaca, 1962. *An analysis of marketing of snapdragons is given in Chapter 14, and grading of this crop is discussed.*
7. Langhans, Robert W., and D. C. Kiplinger, et al., *Easter Lilies—The Culture, Diseases, Insects, and Economics of Easter Lilies*, New York State Extension Service, Ithaca, and Cooperative Extension Service,

Ohio State University, Columbus, 1967. *Preparation of lilies for market is discussed in Chapter 14, and various aspects of marketing lilies are given in Chapter 15.*

8. Laurie, Alex, D. C. Kiplinger, and Kennard S. Nelson, *Commercial Flower Forcing*, Seventh Edition, McGraw-Hill Book Company, New York, 1969. *Reference is made to marketing of each individual crop in chapters 10 through 13. A general discussion of marketing in the flower industry is given in Chapter 14.*

9. Mastalerz, John W., et al., *Geraniums—A Manual on the Culture, Diseases, Insects, Economics, Taxonomy, and Breeding of Geraniums,* Second Edition, Pennsylvania Flower Growers, University Park, 1971. *A detailed discussion of marketing as related to geraniums is given in chapters 31 and 32. The basics of marketing are well covered, and these will apply to any product. Chapters 29 and 30 present a thorough study of geranium product costs. This of course is of interest to the geranium producer, but the methods used may be adapted to some other crops also.*

10. Mastalerz, John W., and Robert W. Langhans, et al., *Roses—A Manual on the Culture, Management, Diseases, Insects, Economics, and Breeding of Greenhouse Roses,* Pennsylvania Flower Growers, University Park, New York State Flower Growers, Inc., Ithaca, and Roses, Inc., Haslett, Michigan, 1969. *Chapter 19, "Post-Harvest Life," is pertinent to marketing. Chapters 37 and 38 explore various possibilities on pricing roses, and Chapter 39 makes some general comments on consumer needs in reference to roses.*

11. McCarthy, E. Jerome, *Basic Marketing: A Managerial Approach*, Richard D. Irwin, Inc., Homewood, Illinois, 1968. *The flower and plant producer needs to know the basics of marketing, because that will allow him to carry out a successful, specific marketing program for his products. This text does cover the basics of marketing clearly and well, but the references to big business and factory-produced hard goods may be distracting. The application to small business and flower and plant marketing is there for the reader who is willing to interpolate a bit.*

12. Miller, Robert O., and D. C. Kiplinger, et al., *Poinsettias—Culture and Use as Potted Plants*, Extension Bulletin, S. B. 15, Agricultural Extension Service, Ohio State University, Columbus, 1963. *Chapters 13 and 14 are concerned primarily with the handling of this product during the marketing phase*

13. Pfahl, Peter B., *The Retail Florist Business*, Second Edition, The Interstate Printers & Publishers, Inc., Danville, Illinois, 1973. *All phases of retail marketing of flowers and plants are discussed in this book.*

INDEX

A

Absolute day-length plants, 174
Account
    information, 19-22
    opening, 19-22
Accountant, 23, 25, 27-28
Air
    carbon dioxide, 165, 203-205, 217
    diffusion into plant, 165
    environment, 163-222
    light transmission, 165
    movement
        natural, 59, 168, 203, 206-207
        ventilation systems, 59-62, 168, 203, 207-208
    oxygen, 165, 206
    problems routed through, 216-218
    temperature, 183-184, 193-194, 200-203, 210-211, 216-217
    water vapor, 165-166, 193-194, 199-203, 210-211, 216-217
Ampere, 40-41
Angstrom units, 167
Azaleas, 87-88, 91, 181, 184

B

Bedding plants, 105-106, 136, 228
Bench drainage, 114, 117, 134
Black cloth, 177-179
Botrytis blight, 210
British thermal unit, 171, 190
Budget, 11-12
Business
    address, 15
    assets, 28-29
    capital improvement, 27-28
    communication, 17-18

    credit policy, 22-23
    expensing, 27-28
    financing, 23-24
    inventory, 28
    liabilities, 28-29
    management, 4-5, 13, 16, 28
    name, 15
    office, 16-17
        accounts payable, 18-19, 28
        accounts receivable, 19-20, 25
        billing, 18-19
        payroll, 18
        purchasing, 18
        records, 16, 19, 27
    taxation, 27
    terms, 19-23

C

Carbohydrates, 168
Carbon dioxide
    photosynthesis, and, 166, 203-205
    stomates, effects on, 165-166, 203
Carnation
    color distribution, 77
    cropping, 77-79
    disease, 136
    lighting, 79, 174
    pinching, 77-79
    rotation, 77-79, 104-105, 108
    temperature, 185
Cement, 35-36
Chain of command, 5-8, 17
Chlorophyll, 168
Chloropicrin, 131
Chrysanthemum cut flower, 79-85, 105-108
    classification system, 82-83
    color distribution, 79
    cropping, 79-85